FULL CIRCLE

BASED ON THE TRUE STORY OF A POLICE
DETECTIVE'S PURSUIT OF A COLOMBIAN
CARTEL QUEEN

Thanks for your support!
Bradley T Wilson

Capt. Bradley T. Wilson

Fulton Books
Meadville, PA

Published by Fulton Books 2024

This story is based on some actual events and the methodology of the Colombian drug cartels in the 1980s and 1990s. It's a creative semifictional account where character names and locations have been changed to protect privacy. In certain cases, changes have also been made to incidents, characters, and time lines for dramatic purposes. Certain incidents and characters may be composites or entirely fictitious.

ISBN 978-1-63985-909-2 (paperback)
ISBN 978-1-63985-910-8 (digital)

Printed in the United States of America

My Family

Monique

Danielle

Erik

Colton

Capri

Bentley

CHAPTER
1

The restaurant was surrounded. Eighteen undercover police detectives took surveillance positions in the restaurant parking lot and across the street, on the upper level of a retail parking structure. I had a view of the restaurant entrance sitting in a nondescript undercover metallic-gray Honda Accord. My hand gripped a 300mm camera. I scanned the area to make sure no one was looking in my direction before I edged the camera out of my open car window.

The mic to the police radio lay in my lap—out of sight from anyone who might take a glance at me. My Colt .45, a semiautomatic handgun, was at the ready, resting on the car seat under my left thigh. As any seasoned detective knew, shoving a Colt .45 in your waistband could get very uncomfortable during an extended surveillance.

It was Thanksgiving night 1987. We were sitting outside the Cali Restaurant on Van Nuys Boulevard in the city of Van Nuys. Our hopeful target was a drug kingpin from Colombia who controlled the distribution of cocaine throughout Western United States. This rarely seen drug mastermind, however, wasn't actually a kingpin. The drug mastermind was a queenpin; Isabella Herrera, the brainy beauty queen from a prominent family in Cali, Colombia.

Shortly after high school, her restless and rebellious spirit propelled her to America. At first, she scraped by with jobs as a waitress and food truck vendor. Then she was lured by a couple of fellow transplanted Colombians to join their import-export business. In a few short years, her CEO-like business skills launched her from a drug mule to one of the main cocaine distribution leaders in the United States, working directly under the Rodriguez brothers in Colombia.

The restaurant surveillance was not spearheaded by the FBI, the DEA, or any other large federal agency. It was led by a six-member narcotic task force of the Torrance Police Department, which is located in a suburb of Los Angeles County.

I felt fortunate to be a part of the task force. Our extensive training and the unique skills of each member resulted in an uncommon success rate in battling the cocaine invasion that had exploded in the US during the mid-1980s.

Isabella first appeared on Torrance Police's radar less than two years prior to this restaurant stakeout, when one of our informants made contact with a drug trafficker who referred to his boss as a high-ranking cartel member and as a very attractive caleña, a woman from Cali, Colombia. During our task force's subsequent surveillances, I spotted Isabella on two occasions—once at Hollywood Park Racetrack and again at a U-Haul lot in Anaheim. But on both occasions, she eluded our shadowing.

At 8:15 p.m. on Thanksgiving of 1987, our next opportunity to tail Isabella appeared to be at hand. A dark blue Ford Aerostar pulled into the restaurant parking lot. A well-dressed Latina passenger in her late twenties stepped out of the van. Detective Bill Mattson was on the eye and was calling the play-by-play of the events on the police radio to us.

"Tommy, can you confirm?"

"It's her," I said. I snapped photos of Isabella as she entered the restaurant.

For the next two hours, Isabella and about seven other people enjoyed the evening, laughing and tipping back a lot of beer. By 10:15 p.m., the group exited the restaurant. Isabella and her driver hopped in the Aerostar and traveled from Van Nuys Boulevard to the I-405. Several detective vehicles trailed them.

The van used erratic anti-surveillance maneuvers—sudden turns, running red lights, etc.—to expose a tail. Isabella turned around in her seat to see if they were being followed. Some of the less-experienced detectives assisting the task force took the bait by visibly following the Aerostar's erratic moves, thereby burning their undercover status.

Isabella knew she was the target of a police surveillance. The Aerostar transitioned to the US 101, then exited and reentered the freeway. Only a few detectives could remain on surveillance without getting burned.

The Aerostar exited the freeway again, and entered a working-class residential area, turning on several different blocks. Isabella continued to look over her shoulder for any following cars. She gave instructions to the driver. He nodded, and the van slowed. Isabella jumped out while it was still moving. She dashed into a front yard and hid behind a large tree.

After considerable time passed, Isabella saw no passing cars in the neighborhood. She removed her shoes and jogged to a nearby Shell gas station. Isabella spotted a Latina in her early fifties filling her gas tank. She approached and addressed her in Spanish.

"Would you do me a favor?"

"That depends on the favor," replied the woman.

Isabella detected the accent. "What part of Colombia are you from?"

"Bogotá," said the woman.

"I'm from Cali. Nice to meet a fellow Colombian."

The woman just smiled. She was still sizing up this stranger who had approached her. Isabella was getting anxious. She rushed to the point.

"I'll fill up your tank and pay you five hundred dollars if you drive me to the Mexican border."

"Right now?" The woman was a bit taken aback.

Isabella nodded. She waited for an answer for what seemed like an eternity.

The woman displayed her own set of street smarts. "Let's see the money."

Isabella reached into her purse and pulled out a bundle of hundreds. The woman stared at the bills.

*****

Meanwhile, the detectives' vehicles roamed the nearby neighborhoods. Frustration mounted. We had the queenpin in our sights, but she was on the verge of slipping away from us yet again. Time was running out. We had to pick up Isabella's trail before she disappeared, perhaps forever.

CHAPTER
2

S mart. Beautiful. Determined. Isabella Herrera was born in and raised by a respectable family just outside of Cali, Colombia. Her parents, Gustavo and Maria, were both highly educated. They owned one of the largest plastic factories in Colombia. They were a success story and had what everyone wanted. Most importantly, they didn't have to worry about money.

Isabella's siblings did not disappoint and followed the path their parents had created for them. Her brother, Eduardo, the oldest, was quite a bit older than her—by fifteen years, to be exact. He had attended all the best schools in Colombia and was a highly paid defense attorney in Bogotá.

Isabella's sister, Gloria, was twelve years senior to her and had also attended Columbia's best schools. Another success story, Gloria became a pediatrician and had set up a practice in the same city. She was another reason everyone around looked at the family in admiration.

It was 1976, and Isabella was set to graduate from high school and continue the family legacy. She had the formula for success embedded in her. Like her siblings, she was graduating at the top of her class. Why would her destiny be any different? She would complete the perfect, successful family picture.

While Isabella was groomed and ready, there was something else. She was different. She had all the traits one would expect from a family that bred success, but Isabella had another layer her siblings didn't possess. On the surface, she seemed the same, but her outgoing personality had always gotten her into a little trouble while growing up. She was a free spirit, but deep down there was something burning within.

In high school, Isabella continued the family tradition and scored off the charts; however, she always wanted more. She was restless and wanted to be different from her siblings. She yearned for the freedom to create her own path.

But her prim upper-class parents would have none of it. Gustavo and Maria were always redirecting Isabella and hoped that her going away to college would settle her down a bit. College was something that was never discussed in their family but was always expected. Isabella was born understanding that this was the path she had to take. It was the path everyone in her family had taken, why would hers be any different?

But Isabella had different plans. She didn't have any interest in college and wanted to travel the world. She wanted to go to America, where several of her older friends lived and were experiencing a different life; a better life for someone like her.

Shortly after graduation, Isabella told her parents that she wasn't going to college but instead was going to the United States. Her parents were devastated. They made demands and insisted, but Isabella stood firm. It was a quality they loved but hated at the same time, a determined free spirit.

They pushed it a step further and told her she would be excluded from any financial support unless she followed their plan. Isabella could not understand her parents' narrow thinking. *It is my life after all. What do they know?*

One evening, when her parents were out with friends, Isabella packed a suitcase and set off to New York. She left a letter for her parents letting them know how much she loved them, even if they couldn't support her decision.

Isabella liked to be in control of her own life, so she had a plan when she left. With a one-way ticket in hand, she had a friend drop her off at the airport. When she landed at JFK, she was met by a childhood friend, Silvia Rodriguez.

Silvia had moved from Colombia to New York with her parents two years earlier. Now on her own, she resided with three other Colombian girls her age in an apartment in Brooklyn. Like most minority communities in New York, the neighborhood was segregated by race and even by what country and city you were from. All three of Silvia's roommates were from Cali, Colombia, and worked as housekeepers or waitresses in the city.

It was late July, and the weather was hot and humid. Silvia had been on her own for about a year now and was proud to be financially independent from her parents. She worked as a housekeeper six days a week at a Marriott nearby. However, she found the winters in New York to be brutally cold, so she hoped to save enough money to move to California within a couple of years.

Because Isabella was educated and interesting, Silvia liked her and enjoyed her company. She told Isabella she was more than welcome to stay but would have to pay a share of the rent when she got on her feet and got a job. She had a small pull-out couch in her bedroom, and that was where Isabella would sleep.

Silvia offered to help Isabella get a housekeeping job, but Isabella felt a waitressing job was substantially better. Because she came from a wealthy family, she just couldn't see herself cleaning someone else's dirty rooms.

Isabella was determined to explore New York City and find a job. She spoke English and Spanish, and quickly found that to be an advantage. Her first days she walked the city streets and picked up job applications at some local restaurants.

The crowded city shocked her, and Isabella was surprised that she didn't like it. It wasn't what she had expected, and she thought she was in over her head. After a couple of days, Isabella received a call from one of the restaurants — a small hole-in-the-wall coffee shop. Conveniently, it was down the street from her new apartment, so she took the job and started working that very week.

Isabella had never had a job, so working was all new to her. The owner of the coffee shop knew she had no experience but was impressed by the way she carried herself. She projected confidence. He also liked that she spoke two languages. She enjoyed talking to customers and really liked the tips. Many of the customers were men on their way to work, and most would flirt with her. Her inherent charisma combined with her bright smile, curvy figure, and tanned skin, never went unnoticed. Now nineteen, Isabella had no desire to have a boyfriend, so she kept the men at bay.

By January the weather turned bitter cold. Snow and icy rain covered the city for days upon days, making her walk to and from work miserable. This was not the life that Isabella dreamed of. She made up her mind that the first chance she got, she would move to California.

CHAPTER
3

In early March 1977, Isabella called an old friend from back home, Laura Valentina, who lived with her husband, Alfredo, in Sylmar, California; a city in northern Los Angeles County. Isabella told Laura how miserable she was living in New York where she struggled with the weather and crowded streets.

Laura was a close friend of Isabella's sister and had gone to school with her. Laura loved Isabella's family and was always especially fond of Isabella. She considered her the little sister she never had. The weather in Sylmar was similar to the weather in Cali, which seemed more and more appealing. Laura invited Isabella out to Sylmar and welcomed her to stay with her and Alfredo until she found her own place.

Isabella knew this was an opportunity she couldn't refuse. Laura had a two-bedroom apartment, and there was plenty of room for her. Laura even offered Isabella a job on one of the four food trucks she and her husband owned.

*****

In mid-April, Isabella was on a United Airlines flight heading to Los Angeles. She was so happy to leave New York and excited to see what Los Angeles had to offer. She was convinced this was the opportunity she had left her family and comfortable life for.

When she landed, the weather was a beautiful seventy-five degrees, and Laura and Alfredo were there to welcome her with open arms. They embraced, got into their car, and then headed north on the I-405 to Sylmar. The drive seemed fast as Laura and Isabella gabbed on and on, catching up on their lives.

As they drove, Isabella was in awe of the new city she found herself in. It was exactly what she was looking for. Laura had been in contact with Isabella's sister, Gloria, and she told Isabella that her family was concerned for her but were less worried when they found out she was going to live with her and Alfredo. Isabella's family had even offered to pay for Isabella's rent, but Laura told them she couldn't accept a penny and was happy to help.

Laura cautiously mentioned, "Your parents said you can go back to Cali anytime. They love you, and want what's best for you—you could still go to college if you wanted to."

Isabella wouldn't hear it. "College is not in my future! It's not what I want! My family doesn't understand me. I want to live in America and live my life the way I want to."

Laura quickly learned this was a touchy subject, so she didn't bring it up again. After all, she was happy to have her childhood friend from Cali living in Sylmar.

When they arrived at Laura's apartment complex, Isabella was thrilled as it turned out to be a townhome with pretty gardens and even a pool. While it didn't compare to the home she grew up in, it was far better than New York, and she was thankful for it.

Isabella accepted Laura's offer to work on one of their food trucks. At four thirty the following morning, the three of them drove to a small run-down warehouse where the four food trucks and two large freezers were stored.

Two employees worked and prepped the food for each truck. Isabella would learn the ropes with Laura and an older male Colombian named Victor. Each truck had its own locations through-out the Valley area of Los Angeles, usually serving construction work-ers, business professionals, and office workers.

While Victor drove, Laura showed Isabella how to prep the food, so they could start selling as soon as they arrived in North

Hollywood. Isabella was looking forward to this new experience. Victor parked the food truck at a large construction site across the street from a twenty-story office building and sounded the musical alarm that alerted everyone they were there. They would spend the next eight hours there selling breakfast and lunch.

Victor did most of the cooking, Laura handled the customers' orders and money, and by lunchtime, Isabella was already comfortable working the window; taking orders, collecting money, and serving patrons. Isabella learned quickly and was very capable. At two in the afternoon, they returned to the warehouse, resupplied their truck, and ordered food for the following day.

Isabella continued to work hard and really enjoyed meeting people from all walks of life. After six months, Laura and Alfredo let Isabella have her own food truck.

Isabella and another younger Colombian woman, Juanita, were given their own route in the Valley. The opportunity excited Isabella and Juanita, and they became fast friends. It was another new beginning, and Isabella decided it was a good time to move out. She didn't want to overstay her welcome and since she and Juanita were already working together, they decided they might as well live together too. They found a modest two-bedroom townhouse in North Hollywood.

For the next five years, Isabella and Juanita worked their food truck route, covering construction sites and high-rise business offices. During this time, Isabella met a lot of fellow Colombians in the Valley. She frequented the nightclubs in Hollywood and in the Valley and made many new friends. She enjoyed everything the city had to offer, but typical of Isabella, she wanted more out of life. She wanted to live in a nicer place, and she wanted a nicer car.

Isabella realized that continuing to work for Laura and Alfredo wasn't going to give her the life she wanted, so she brainstormed possible ways to make more money. She was certainly smart enough, but she also knew that she needed money to make money. Unfortunately, she spent everything she made and had no savings. Soon, however, a tantalizing opportunity would arise.

CHAPTER
4

One hot summer day, two good-looking Colombian men approached Isabella's food truck. They wore tailored business suits, and she was convinced they worked in one of the high-rises nearby. They ordered some food and couldn't help but notice her beauty and graceful confidence. They flirted with her, and she flirted right back.

Isabella loved the exchange. The men introduced themselves as Andres and Diego. Isabella saw Diego's dimples and was immediately drawn to him. Andres was handsome too, but he didn't have the same charm, plus Diego was younger and closer to her age. Andres, however, seemed to take more of an interest in her. Because both men were from Cali, Colombia, they had a lot in common.

When their order was up, Isabella noticed the wad of hundreds they pulled from their pockets. *Who carries this kind of money around?* she thought, and then she convinced herself they must be powerful businessmen. After they paid, they continued to chat for thirty more minutes about family, friends, and places they had frequented back home.

Over the next month, both men visited Isabella's food truck a few times a week. Isabella looked forward to their visits and would shout out in excitement to Juanita whenever she saw them coming.

"Look who's coming!" she would say in a giddy schoolgirl voice.

Juanita would tease, "You're going to marry one of those men someday!"

But Isabella didn't like the sound of that. She had other plans. In fact, she didn't want to be in a relationship at all. She wanted to prove her parents wrong and become successful her own way. Having a boyfriend or a husband would only be a distraction and would prevent her from reaching her goal.

One day Andres ordered his usual, and they had their typical flirty exchange, but this time, Andres looked at Isabella differently and said, "Isabella, I really like you. I have never met anyone quite like you." He admired her outgoing personality and her take-charge attitude.

Isabella was concerned because she wasn't interested. She politely responded, "Thank you," and tried not to send him the wrong message.

Over the next month, only Andres visited her food truck. Isabella wondered where Diego had gone. "Why doesn't Diego come by anymore?"

"He's been working hard," Andres responded.

"What exactly do you do?" Isabella asked.

He merely responded, "We're in the import-export business." Then he asked, "Would you like to come work with us? I have no idea what you make selling food from this truck, but I can guarantee you would make much more with us."

While Isabella was excited about such an opportunity, she also knew older men like Andres were always trying to get into her pants, and she was apprehensive about Andres's real reason for offering her a job. Isabella boldly asked, "Are we talking about a real job, or are you trying to get me to go out with you? Sorry, but I have to know your real intentions."

Andres laughed. "I know that I've made the right decision about offering you a real job. I promise you, it's an opportunity that will give you a better life." Andres told Isabella that he liked her brash, straightforward personality and that he had no interest in getting together with her. "This is all business," he confirmed.

Relieved, Isabella asked, "What sort of work will I be doing?

"You will work directly for Diego."

Isabella liked the sound of that. "What do you import and export anyway?"

Andres told her that it was domestic products and if she accepted the job, she would learn more about it. Excited, Isabella accepted the position on the spot. Andres told Isabella, "Diego will be getting ahold of you in the next couple weeks to set up a meeting. He will then walk you through the job. I have a feeling you'll love it."

Three weeks went by, and Isabella didn't see or hear from Diego or Andres. She figured that they no longer wanted her to work for them. Then one morning Diego appeared at the lunch truck.

"Are you still interested in the position? We can talk about it tonight, if you're free."

"I'll be off at four!" she quickly responded. This felt like the opportunity of a lifetime.

Diego gave Isabella the name and address of a restaurant called the Scorpion in North Hollywood. "Meet me there at six, and don't be late," he said.

*****

After work, Isabella rushed home to shower and get ready to meet Diego. Not sure how to dress, she finally settled on a flowy white blouse and a new pair of fitted jeans. Now twenty-five, everything about Isabella projected beauty. She looked at herself in the mirror, applied some light-colored lipstick, primped her long, cascading hair one last time, and walked to her car.

Isabella quickly drove to the Scorpion, arriving twenty minutes early. She entered the restaurant and scanned the room, but Diego was nowhere to be seen.

A waitress approached her. "Would you like to be seated?" she asked politely.

"I'm meeting someone, but I'm early. I'll wait in the bar."

Isabella found a seat at the bar and gazed through the window overlooking the parking lot.

"What will you have?" the bartender asked.

"I'll take a Diet Coke."

Isabella then spotted Diego at a pay phone adjacent to the restaurant. *What is he doing out there?* she wondered. She watched him carefully as he moved his hands wildly while he spoke on the phone. *Who is he talking to?* Diego stayed on the phone for about five minutes, hung up, and then made another quick call. *How strange,* she thought.

When Diego hung up, he glanced over the parking lot and then entered the restaurant. Isabella called, "Diego!" to get his attention. He immediately made eye contact with her, noting how unbelievably beautiful she was. He approached and asked her to follow him to a table.

Diego passed up several empty tables near the front of the restaurant and led Isabella to a booth at the back.

"Why are we sitting way back here?" Isabella asked.

"I want privacy."

They exchanged small talk and Diego explained to Isabella that not everyone was interested in the type of work he did, but he hoped she would be on board after she saw what it entailed. Isabella's head was exploding with questions.

"What exactly do you do in the company? What will I be doing? Will I be working with you or Andres?"

"I will explain everything to you after we make a pickup. I want you to see what type of work you'll be doing," he said, hoping she would be satisfied with his simple response. "Are you ready to go?"

CHAPTER
5

Isabella was not usually satisfied with a vague response when she asked a question. She was confused and uncertain, but she agreed. Diego directed Isabella to get into his car and they left the restaurant.

As he drove out of the parking lot, Isabella immediately noticed Diego acting peculiar. He looked in his rearview mirror, long and hard. When they approached a red traffic light, he pulled into the left-turn lane, looked both ways for traffic, then ran the red light. Isabella's heart was racing.

"Are you crazy? You just ran a red light!"

Diego casually responded, "I know I did. It's all part of the job."

Isabella's mind was racing almost as fast as her heart. *Maybe this job is not for me if I have to worry about getting killed in a traffic accident.* Then a second later, she argued in her head, *Maybe this is all worth it if I can make more money.*

Suddenly, Diego checked his rearview mirror again and sped up—they had to be going over 60 mph now. He approached another red light, but this time traffic was backed up. Without skipping a beat, he drove over to the curb lane with barely enough room to squeeze by. Diego slowed down, looked both ways, and ran another red light.

Isabella gripped the armrest tightly and pressed one foot on the floorboard to steady herself. She was scared. She demanded, "Stop the fucking car, Diego! You're going to kill us!"

Diego continued to be perfectly calm. He laughed at her. "Don't worry about it. This is part of the job."

Diego approached the freeway, driving well above the speed limit. Although the on-ramp was backed up, he jerked the steering wheel and moved the car over to the right shoulder, passed all the cars, and entered the freeway.

At this point, Isabella was screaming and wondering how she had gotten herself in this mess. He quickly accelerated and drove in the fast lane for about a mile. All the while, Diego continuously looked in his rearview mirror.

"Is someone following us?" Isabella shouted.

"I don't think so," Diego casually answered.

He changed lanes, weaving in and out of traffic. He drove back into the fast lane, then suddenly crossed all four lanes and took an off-ramp. Again, Diego continued to look into his rearview mirror.

Isabella demanded again, "Pull over and let me out!"

"Don't worry, Isabella. You will soon understand why I'm driving this way."

Isabella glanced back and noticed there were no cars behind them. Diego slowed a bit and parked in a large shopping mall in the city of Burbank. He got out of the car and told Isabella to do the same. She followed him to a pay phone outside a Vons grocery store.

Diego made a phone call while Isabella waited nearby. She noticed he spoke in Spanish. She heard him say *aquí*, which meant "here." He then described what he and Isabella looked like, and what they were wearing. He ended the phone call by telling the person he would be waiting.

Now Isabella wanted answers. "What is going on, Diego? I deserve to know. This is not what I signed up for."

"Please don't worry, Isabella. I will tell you everything, but you must be patient. My client will be here soon. I'll fill you in when we are done."

Soon, a young Latino wearing a bright-red baseball cap arrived in an older model Chevy van. He got out, walked over to Diego, greeted him, and took his keys. Isabella watched with a keen eye as the man walked over to Diego's car, jumped in, and then drove away.

"What's going on?" Isabella asked. She couldn't explain it, but the situation just felt wrong.

"Patience," Diego said. He told Isabella his client was dropping off some merchandise for him to export. "It's all part of the business," Diego said.

Twenty minutes passed, and the Latino returned with Diego's car. He parked, got out, and walked over to Diego. Tossing the keys back to Diego he said, "Take care," and he walked back to his own van and drove away.

"Get in the car," Diego instructed in a serious tone. He started the engine, and they left the parking lot.

Isabella looked in the back seat for the merchandise Diego had talked about, but saw nothing. She was becoming more and more suspicious about what they were really doing. "Where's the merchandise?" Isabella asked.

"It's in the trunk. I am going to take you to one of my businesses in South Gate. When we get there, I will explain everything."

Isabella noticed that Diego was no longer driving fast, nor was he running any red traffic lights. And even though he continued to look in his rearview mirror, she was much more comfortable now.

It took about forty-five minutes to get to South Gate, due to the heavy traffic. Diego pulled into the parking lot of a small strip mall and told Isabella he had to make a phone call. He got out of the car and made the call at a pay phone, which only lasted five seconds. He then got back into his car and drove about a mile to an auto body business.

When they arrived, Isabella noticed that the auto shop was closed. A gray-haired Latino opened the iron gate that led to some garages. Diego drove in and the man closed and locked the gate behind them. Diego proceeded to the rear of the business and into an open garage. The man followed them into the garage, pulled down the metal roll door, and secured it with a padlock.

The uncertainty of what was going on caused fear to set in again for Isabella. Her mind was racing. She knew, deep down, that what they were doing must be illegal. Diego could see this in her eyes and tried to ease her fears by telling her not to worry, but he sounded like a broken record.

Diego introduced Isabella to the elderly man, Miguel, and said he was one of his employees. Diego then told Miguel, "That's all for tonight. You can leave."

"Gracias, señor," he responded and left.

Isabella was confused at this point. She still had not seen any merchandise. Diego walked to the trunk of his car as Isabella stood next to the passenger door. He opened the trunk, reached in, and grabbed something Isabella could not see because the trunk was blocking her view. Diego then tossed a bundle of something in her direction.

"Catch it!" Diego exclaimed, "This is your first day's pay."

Isabella reached out and caught the bundle with one hand. She looked down at it and was shocked. "Is this real?" she asked.

"Of course, it is," Diego responded, "Make sure you count it. There should be five thousand dollars."

Isabella was excited but tried to remain calm. "Five thousand dollars! I get five thousand dollars for what we just did? This is crazy, Diego!"

"Enjoy it because the pay is normally much less, but we really want you on our team."

Diego motioned to Isabella to come toward the trunk of the car. Her eyes widened in disbelief. There she saw bundles upon bundles of cash. Diego told Isabella they needed to count them and make sure each bundle contained exactly five thousand dollars. He walked over to a door inside the garage, which led to a large room containing nothing but two long tables. Isabella followed Diego and noticed two small machines on top of the tables.

Diego said, "These are money counters—a lot faster than counting by hand."

"How much are we talking about?" asked Isabella.

"One point five."

"One hundred fifty thousand?"

"One point five million."

Isabella's initial shock gave way to a sinking feeling in the pit of her stomach. She was not naive. She mumbled to herself, "Drug money."

Diego could tell it had suddenly all become clear to her. He looked right at her and said, "Yes, Isabella. Welcome to the Cali Drug Cartel." He gently grabbed her hand and told her not to say a thing until he had explained the business to her.

"What you did tonight is what your job will be within the organization. You will be a distributer. The money we collected tonight is from the import of millions of dollars of cocaine from Colombia into the American drug market. It is extremely important the Cali cartel bosses receive their money back for the sale of the cocaine they imported."

Diego continued, "Tonight, we need to count the money and then contact the bosses back in Cali and let them know how much money we picked up. Then the bosses will give us a pager number of the person we'll pass the money on to." Isabella listened carefully to every word.

"At times, you'll pick up millions of dollars in kilos of cocaine instead of money, but you'll know beforehand if you're picking up money or product." He referred to the cocaine as product. "Once you're established, you'll have to rent a house, an apartment or a business establishment to store the product before passing it on. If that's the case, you'll need a couple of people to guard the product until it can be moved to the next location. These people are called mules."

Isabella started to say something, but Diego cut her off. "Let me finish!" He continued, "With any successful organization, there has to be checks and balances. In this business, there are severe consequences when someone steals money or product. As long as you don't take anything that doesn't belong to you, you'll have nothing to worry about."

Diego also explained another consequence to this job. "Let's say you get sloppy and are arrested, and the money or product you are responsible for gets seized by the police. Not only will the police investigate you, but the cartel will also make sure you weren't involved in the loss of their property."

Diego told her that recruiting people she could trust would be the most important part of the job. He emphasized, "You will be the one the Cali bosses hold accountable for any deals gone wrong."

Isabella asked, "How will they hold me accountable?"

"There are many ways. One, the organization could kidnap your family back in Colombia and—"

"Kidnap my family? What would they do with them?" Isabella asked.

"Threaten them, hurt them, and sometimes make them disappear."

Isabella knew what this meant—death. She didn't like the sound of this. Diego told Isabella that if she decided to work in the organization, it would take years for her to learn all aspects of the business. If she did well, she would have the chance, not only to make a lot of money, but also rise in the hierarchy of the Cali cartel. "Being a pretty girl like yourself is a big advantage. The cops won't suspect you. Neither will our rivals. You could really make it work, but it won't be easy."

Diego and Isabella spent the next few hours placing one bundle after another in the money counters until they finished counting— one and a half million dollars. Isabella had never seen this much cash in one place! Diego then moved a rug and opened a hidden compartment in a false floor in the room. Together they placed all the money and the money counters inside, out of sight.

Diego said, "You know, if you take this job, you will be working closely with me until I feel you can do it on your own. I'll make sure you're safe and learn everything you need to know." He then told her he would set her up with a new identity and new car.

With their business now done for the night; Diego drove Isabella back to the restaurant. To Isabella, the drive back seemed much longer as she contemplated Diego's offer. They pulled into the parking lot and sat in silence.

Diego waited, then asked, "What do you think? Do you want in?"

Isabella's head swirled. *The money I could make would change my life, but I would never want to hurt or shame my family.* She stared at

Diego without saying a word. Finally, she responded, "I need twenty-four hours."

Diego smiled and nodded. "I'll pick you up at your house at 4:00 p.m. tomorrow. You can give me your answer then. I'll contact my boss, David, and tell him about the money we picked up after I get your answer."

CHAPTER
6

T he next day's drive to Santa Monica was a long one, but that was the way she wanted it. Isabella needed a morning of solitude to make up her mind. Back in Colombia, when she wanted to set aside a time and place to ponder things, she would drive down to the Rio Pance.

She loved to gaze at the clear, cool waters and surrounding greenery. Nothing was better for relaxing her mind and pinpointing her thoughts. The vast Pacific Ocean reminded Isabella of the Rio Pance. She could have stayed for hours on a Palisades Park bench perched on the edge of the Santa Monica cliffs, overlooking the beach.

On this day, her thoughts were heavy. She had a chance to prove her parents wrong and prove that she could make it on her own, that there could be more than one path in life for a young woman, more than getting a college diploma, having a respectable job, and being a dutiful wife.

She was aware of the risks, including jail and retribution from her bosses. But her intuition told her that she could be a success. She trusted her smarts and her determination. If she approached it as a business, with all the efficiency and caution it demanded, she could reap benefits that couldn't be found anywhere else. Perhaps she could even make enough money over the years to allow her to fade out of the drug world and retire on her earnings.

Still, it was no easy decision. She racked her brain to come up with a better alternative. Would it be wiser to decline and explore other opportunities? But no matter how long and hard Isabella reflected on this problem, there was one crucial aspect that she could not have foreseen.

When Isabella left Colombia in 1976, her native country was still more than a decade away from the widespread public violence that plagued cities such as Cali and Medellín. At that time, most of the cocaine was still grown in countries like Bolivia, Ecuador, and Chile. So she was not exposed to the local brutality of cocaine traffickers fighting over territory, influencing local authorities, and silencing protesters.

According to an investigative report by the *Los Angeles Times*, Cali drug lords would toss the mutilated bodies of enemies—the disappeared—in the Cauca River. From the late 1980s, so many corpses floated down the river that vultures gathered at an eddy in the nearby town of Marsella.

The *Times* reported that between 1988 and 1991, over 219 victims were recovered from Marsella, which was only a small fraction of the number that passed by the small coffee town and continued downriver.

The road ahead for Isabella was going to be rougher than she ever could have imagined.

CHAPTER
7

Diego showed up at Isabella's townhouse the following day promptly at 4:00. As he pulled in the driveway, she ran out to meet him. She got in the car, fastened her seat belt, then turned and looked at Diego. "I'm in," she simply said.

After a quick nod and a smile, Diego wasted little time in training Isabella; and from this point on, Isabella studied Diego's every move. He drove a mile and pulled over at a pay phone to contact his boss back home in Colombia to tell him how much money they had picked up the day before. He put some quarters in the phone and dialed a number, then hung up.

"I just paged my boss this phone number to call me back on," he said. Twenty minutes crept by, and still, there was no return call. Diego explained to Isabella, "This happens. Sometimes, they are busy and can't get right back to me. Let's get back in the car. We'll try again in ten minutes."

Diego drove a few miles down the road and pulled over at another bank of pay phones near a grocery store. He again told Isabella to come with him, but this time, he had her make the call. She called the pager and left the number to the pay phone they were at, and then hung up.

Another fifteen minutes went by, and finally the phone rang. Diego answered the phone and told his boss how much money he had picked up. He then told him about Isabella being on board.

Diego held the receiver out toward Isabella and said, "He wants to speak to you." Isabella nervously took the phone.

Diego's boss introduced himself as David, greeted her kindly, and congratulated her for joining the team. He said, "Diego is very knowledgeable about the business. I advise you to pay close attention to everything he is going to teach you."

"Thank you for the opportunity. I won't let you down," she said and then returned the phone to Diego.

Diego said, "I'll set up Isabella during the next week. My facilitator should be calling me tomorrow." He then hung up.

Diego and Isabella got back into Diego's car, and he began to drive Isabella back to her house. When they were a couple of miles away, Diego started driving erratically again. He looked in his rearview mirror as he ran red traffic lights or suddenly switched lanes. He was looking for anyone who might be following them.

Isabella asked, "Why are you doing this now? We don't have any money or merchandise to worry about."

He explained, "No one should know where you live. I want to make sure cops or anyone else aren't following us. You will need to drive like this each and every time you go home."

As they got closer, Diego began to drive at a high rate of speed and ran a red light, drove down an alley, and pulled over to the curb to watch traffic. "Everything appears to be clear," he said. He then drove to Isabella's house and dropped her off. "I will pick you up here at noon tomorrow to pass the money on to the next person," he said, then he sped away.

*****

The following morning, Isabella woke up at four thirty and drove to Laura and Alfredo's warehouse, just as she normally would, to prepare her food truck for the day. As she entered the building, she saw Laura and Alfredo across the way and approached them.

Isabella was anxious about telling them that she wouldn't be working for them anymore. After all, they had made her dream of living in California possible, and she didn't want to be ungrateful.

Not one to beat around the bush, Isabella quickly broke the news to her friends.

"I hope you understand how much I appreciate everything you have done for me. My friend Diego offered me a job at his import-export business, and I will be earning a lot more money than I do here. There is a huge opportunity for me to move up in this business and make some really good money in the future," she told them.

Laura and Alfredo were stunned. Laura asked, "Are you sure about this, Isabella? It all seems so sudden."

"Please don't worry. I have a good feeling about this," Isabella said.

Noticing that Isabella seemed concerned for their business, Laura wanted to put her mind at ease. "We'll be okay. We have enough people to cover your truck. Please tell me, Isabella, what's the name of this business?"

Isabella brushed over the details and said, "It's a new, start-up business—and there's not a name for it yet." She could tell Laura and Alfredo seemed confused and concerned by her vague answer. Isabella took a step back before adding, "I'm very sorry to say this, but I have to start my new job today at noon, so I cannot work today."

"Today?" Alfredo asked.

Feeling even more surprised, but keeping in mind how much she admired her childhood friend, Laura told her, "This is so sudden, Isabella, but if this is what you want to do, we understand. If it doesn't work out though, and you need your job back, we will always be here for you. We love you and want you to be happy and successful."

As she left, Isabella thanked them for supporting her decision. The sun was just rising, so Isabella drove to a nearby coffee shop for some breakfast. The first day of her new life was about to begin.

CHAPTER

8

I barely knew him while he was alive, but I felt that his spirit had passed to mine two deep-rooted traits; a love of the sea and a tough, never-quit mindset. My grandfather Tommy Greer Sr. operated a tugboat on the southern coast of Ireland in the early twentieth century. During the Irish revolt of British rule, Tommy Greer Sr. and his older brothers joined the underground resistance to fight for independence. In an altercation with British soldiers, two of his brothers were killed, and Tommy Greer Sr. became a wanted man. He was forced into hiding.

Tommy Greer Sr. first attempted to escape to America on a ship embarking from Dublin. Before he reached the docks, he received word that British officials were waiting for him. He dodged the British but had to wait another six months before his next escape attempt.

His very own seafaring grandfather smuggled the fugitive Tommy Greer Sr. in a coast guard boat to Germany. From there, Tommy Greer Sr. eventually made it to America, settling in Redondo Beach, California, to be near the sea and a cousin who served as a priest at St. James Church. He later married an Irish girl from Donegal named Mary, and they had seven children. One of the daughters, Shannon Greer, was to be my mother.

Times were hard for the immigrant family. Tommy Greer Sr. worked in a factory, pouring molten steel. Mary worked as a maid, cleaning homes. Both parents drank heavily. Their cramped house was full of chaos.

Shannon, my mother, married young and had two children by the time she was eighteen years old. Her husband left soon thereafter, and she raised the children on her own. She married again at twenty-eight. Two more children were added to the family—me, Tommy Greer Jr., and my big sister Cait. However, my father left us to live with another woman before I was born.

Now my mother was stuck with four kids and could barely make ends meet. With a ninth-grade education, her opportunities were limited. She worked as a waitress at a coffee shop and sometimes she would take on a second waitressing job to support her family.

The five of us occupied a two-bedroom apartment behind a beauty shop in Redondo Beach. When I was six years old, my grandfather Tommy Greer Sr. was killed in a car accident. My grandmother, Mary Greer, then moved in with us. Now six people tried to navigate their daily lives in the crowded apartment.

My mother did everything she could to protect us and provide for us. We never had any money to spare, but I never knew it. I thought it was normal for families to eat SpaghettiOs for dinner every night.

By the time I got into middle school, my mother married again. My stepfather, John, was twenty years her senior. He was a nice enough guy, but by this time, all of us kids were fairly independent and didn't want another adult in the house telling us what to do. We moved from the two-bedroom apartment to a five-bedroom house on a busy street in Redondo Beach.

Shortly after moving into the new house, John lost his job and our family scraped by to stay in the house. My mother rented out bedrooms to relatives and sometimes to strangers. Many of the people who lived in the house over the years were alcoholics, drug addicts, and people with mental health problems.

One of my aunts came to live with us directly from a mental institution. If she failed to take her prescribed medications, she could launch into bizarre or volatile behavior. On one occasion, she stood outside our front door stark naked. Another time, she chased my sister Cait into the backyard, waving a machete. I was able to tackle my aunt before she did any harm.

I promised myself that when I grew up and had a family of my own, I would provide my kids with a safe and stable home; the opposite of my home. There might have been a growing resentment as I endured these precarious events, but I later realized that such experiences gave me a certain level of maturity and inner strength that most of my peers did not possess. These qualities proved essential for a budding LAPD police officer in a city racked with murder, rape, and drugs.

Meanwhile, I found solace at the beach. From an early age, I enjoyed swimming, surfing, playing beach volleyball, and riding bikes along the beach. Sports provided another outlet for my energy and frustrations. As an athlete, I loved the competition, physical challenges, and camaraderie. During my high school years, I was an outstanding three-sport athlete and received many awards and accolades in football, basketball, and volleyball.

I continued playing football at a local junior college. I enjoyed some success on the field, but over time, life took me in another direction. During my college days, I not only played football but also had a full class load and held down two part-time jobs. I partied a lot with my roommates and started getting into fights. I felt a little overwhelmed and found my pent-up anger getting the best of me. Someone noticed that I was going in the wrong direction.

Mike Kauffman lived down the street from where I grew up. He was an LAPD officer who followed my sporting achievements in the local newspaper. He was a hulk of a man who could bench press 485 pounds. He had converted his garage into a weightlifting room and allowed me to work out there because he knew I didn't have enough money to join a gym.

One day, Mike took me aside and got in my face. Frankly, he scared the shit out of me. Mike told me he heard I was partying too much and getting into fights. He leaned in close and grabbed the collar of my shirt to get my undivided attention. Mike was giving me a wake-up call.

As he stared directly in my eyes, he said, "I am not going to let you go down that path! You need to knock this shit off and grow up, or you'll have to deal with me!" He said I had a lot going for me and suggested I should become a cop. He encouraged me to take the entrance exam as soon as I could.

Mike had given me something to think about. Perhaps with the police force, I could find that same sense of teamwork, camaraderie, and physical challenge that I enjoyed in sports. Perhaps, too, the police force could provide a certain sense of structure and stability, which I never really had growing up.

During my first year in college, I happened to meet another person who would change my life forever. After football practice, I would go to the local Subway. A friend managed the shop and would give me free sandwiches—at a time when I was usually strapped for cash.

One day, I walked into Subway and saw a new worker behind the counter. She made a sandwich for me. Her name was Nicole. Her beauty and grace were mesmerizing. She was tall, athletic, and had an engaging personality.

Over the next few weeks, I asked Nicole out on a date on at least seven separate occasions. Each time Nicole said no. I was baffled at being turned down by her as we flirted a lot and we seemed to really hit it off. A few weeks later, my persistence finally paid off and Nicole and I finally had our first date.

In Nicole, I knew I had met the dream of my life. We dated for about a year, and I soon realized that a woman like her would not marry a guy like me until I had a career and a mission in life. I brought up the idea of becoming a police officer. She supported it wholeheartedly.

Mike Kauffman advised me to apply for the Torrance Police Department, which had a reputation for being an outstanding proactive department. I applied but was rejected during the background phase. I was twenty-one years old at the time, and Torrance PD had many other mature applicants from whom to choose. But Mike wouldn't let me stay disappointed long. He encouraged me to take the test for the Los Angeles Police Department. This time, I was accepted.

Nicole helped me prepare for the police academy by stenciling all my workout clothes with my name on the front and back, keeping in mind the exact criteria determined by the academy. She further helped me save my scarce funds by shaving my head in the academy's style.

I excelled in the physical training of the academy and graduated with Nicole and Mike at my side. I spent a total of two years in the West Los Angeles division and the Seventy-Seventh division (Watts). I worked hard to hone my crime-fighting skills. While I knew it was a valuable experience to be on patrol and respond to emergency incidents on a call-by-call basis, I was driven to move up the ranks and work in an undercover detail, which had more emphasis on teamwork and building up cases over the long-term.

Upon completing the one-year probation period with LAPD, Mike advised me to make a lateral transfer to the Torrance PD. I was able to do just that. Torrance PD gave me the opportunity I was looking for. I put together a record of exemplary arrests. I bonded well with the other officers, many of whom grew up in the same South Bay area as I did. Then I was selected to join Sgt. Dave Tilly's undercover narcotic task force.

Little did I know, I would soon come face-to-face with one of the highest-ranking Colombian drug lords. But for now, we both had some on-the-job training to accomplish.

CHAPTER
9

Isabella lingered at the coffee shop, eating her breakfast. The appointment with Diego wasn't until noon. She sat at a booth by herself and gazed out the window watching all the people getting ready for the day. Her mind wandered to where life was taking her after this point. While she knew she was about to get involved in some dangerous activity, with the risk also came an adrenaline rush. The potential for a lucrative payoff only added to the edgy excitement.

Isabella finished her breakfast and drove home. About a mile away from her house, she started driving in an anti-surveillance manner using the driving techniques Diego had showed her. She did not see anyone following her, so she continued to her house and went inside.

At noon, Diego knocked on Isabella's front door. Isabella rushed to the door and opened it. As usual, they spoke in their native tongue. Diego said, "Let's go." Isabella grabbed her purse, then closed and locked the door behind her. They were walking down the path leading to the street when Diego threw his keys to her and said, "You drive."

As Isabella got into the driver's side, he said, "Get used to the car—because it's yours."

Astonished, Isabella replied, "I already have a car. Why would you give me a car?"

"Your car is registered in your name with your address. This car is registered in another name with a PO box. I work with a facilitator who picks up all the mail from this PO box and pays the bills for many people in the organization—you know, like car registrations and rentals for houses, apartments, and businesses. The facilitator also has connections to create new identities and get our people new driver's licenses. This is important because you may be stopped or interviewed by the police and you will need to use your new identity. Our real identities are hidden."

Diego handed Isabella a piece of paper with a name and pager number scribbled on it. "The facilitator's name is Gustavo Gonzales. He's expecting a call from you," he said.

"I'll call him the first chance I get."

Diego directed Isabella to drive to the same bank of pay phones they used the other night.

Diego said, "We need to pass on the money we picked up to the next courier. It's important to do this quickly, so you aren't responsible for it. If the police somehow get hold of the money or cocaine, or you get ripped off by another trafficker, then the Cali bosses will hold you accountable."

"That's doesn't seem fair."

Diego agreed it was a drawback to the business but offered another perspective. "It's one way of keeping everyone honest. Now you see why it's important to only hire people you completely trust. If anyone ever steals from you, you'll need to make a quick example of them."

Isabella was confused. "What do you mean, an example—how would I do that?"

Diego explained, "You would need to call David immediately and explain your concerns. David has direct contact with all the bosses. Once David is made aware of any compromises, he will investigate. If he discovered that you got ripped off, then he will put a plan of action together."

"What would he do? He's in Colombia after all. How could he possibly hold someone accountable in the United States?"

"There are many ways the cartel handles these situations. They have serious muscle in the United States with affiliates who deal with suspected thieves. Sometimes they'll send a hit squad. If they're lucky, the hit squad will kill them quickly," Diego said, "If they aren't lucky, they will be made an example of—They'll get tortured, or they'll kidnap and kill their family." He looked directly at Isabella and said, "The cartel is ruthless."

This realization sent shivers down Isabella's spine. But for now, she had to refocus since she was within a mile of the pay phones, and she needed to pay attention in case someone was following them. She entered the freeway and merged into traffic, then she quickly changed lanes. She was getting the hang of this new way of driving and liked it.

As she maneuvered into other lanes, she constantly checked her rearview and side mirrors to see if anyone was following behind. At the next exit, she cut across the lanes and got off the freeway. At the bottom of the off-ramp, she checked and confirmed that no one was following her. She made a sharp right turn, sped through a gas station, and entered the parking lot with the pay phones.

Isabella shifted the car to park, and they both looked over the parking lot to make sure it was clear. They exited the car and approached the pay phones. Diego gave Isabella the pager number for the next person to drop the money off to. She dialed the number, entered the pay phone number she was using, hung up, and waited for a return call.

While waiting, Diego explained that he would answer the phone because he needed to introduce her to the person calling, otherwise the caller would just hang up. Diego had been doing business with this person for some time. His name was Dominick.

"If anyone other than Dominick shows up today, we'll forget about the drop-off and get the hell out of here," Diego said. There was no room for mistakes.

Right then, the pay phone rang. Diego answered and recognized Dominick's voice. In Spanish, Diego explained to him who Isabella was and let him know that he would be dealing with her from this point forward. Diego told Dominick his location and asked him how long it would take him to drive there.

Dominick replied, "About an hour and a half."

"I'll be waiting for your call," Diego said and hung up.

Diego then explained to Isabella that this was the best time for them to conduct business because of rush hour traffic. "It's difficult for someone to follow you when the streets are busy," he said. He suggested they get a bite to eat at a nearby restaurant while they waited.

*****

While at dinner, Diego went in more depth about how the Cali Drug Cartel was run, explaining that the drug business was run like many other successful businesses. "There are levels of hierarchy within the organization—everyone knows their responsibilities and must carry them out. The Cali cartel is run by the Rodriguez brothers, Gilberto and Miguel."

Diego continued, "Our positions are the most dangerous because we're the ones who have to move the product from Colombia to and throughout the United States." Isabella listened attentively as Diego spoke. There was a lot to learn. "If you get caught by the police, the cartel bosses expect you to say nothing about the organization and their operations."

"How would people back in Colombia have control over what we tell the police in the United States?" Isabella asked.

"When someone in the organization is arrested in the US, the first thing the bosses do is contact one of the attorneys on their payroll. The attorney's job is to represent you but also keep you quiet. Once you have an attorney, the police can't talk to you without the attorney's permission."

Isabella asked, "What's stopping someone from refusing an attorney from the cartel and speaking to the cops?"

Diego warned, "That would be a big mistake. The attorney or someone else from the organization will find a way to contact you in jail and that's when they'll tell you your family in Colombia will be in jeopardy."

Isabella wasn't comfortable with this scenario at all. She loved her family and wouldn't want to cause them any harm. Diego tried to dispel any doubts she had. "Law enforcement hasn't figured out our methods yet, so you won't get caught unless you get careless."

Isabella pondered Diego's statement, and then her mind shifted to a more strategic side of the spectrum, "How can I get to David's level in the organization?"

Diego eased the tension and smiled. "I've been in the business for five years now, and I just got to my current position. Don't get your hopes up, Isabella, there aren't any women higher than a mule in the Cali cartel," he said.

Isabella, half joking, responded, "I'll have to change that!"

Diego laughed. "Good luck."

Isabella learned that Diego's boss, David, told him to recruit a female Colombian. David felt that a female would be less suspicious and because Diego recruited Isabella, he was promoted.

An hour and a half went by quickly. Diego's pager went off, "Dominick is in the area," he said. Diego picked up the tab and they left.

Isabella was driving and Diego directed her to go past the parking lot where the pay phones were, so they could get a good look at Dominick. They checked for people following them and then saw Dominick near the pay phones looking out over the parking lot.

Diego instructed Isabella, "We need to make sure he's alone. Pull over. I want to watch him until I feel comfortable. I always like to protect myself with one extra layer of precaution."

Once they were convinced Dominick was by himself, he told Isabella to drive three blocks east into a Vons parking lot. There they could call Dominick and instruct him to come to them. Diego said, "This way, as we see him drive into the parking lot, we can be certain no one is following him."

Isabella quickly realized that she could never be too cautious in a job like this. She was impressed. Diego provided the kind of insight only someone with experience could have offered. As they arrived in the Vons's parking lot, they looked for anything or anyone suspicious. They saw nothing, so they parked near a set of pay phones.

Diego called Dominick's pager and left the pay phone number. Two minutes later, the phone rang. It was Dominick. Diego told him to meet us at our new location.

He hung up and said, "There will be times when you don't know the person you will pick up money from, or drop off money to. In those cases, you will need to describe what you look like and what you are wearing. You may have to describe the car you're driving too."

While they waited for Dominick, Diego continued to inform Isabella. "If you ever feel slightly suspicious about anything, then you need to walk away or get in your car and leave. Sometimes a client may be dirty and may be working with undercover cops to set you up. If that's the case, then drive far away and call me or David when it's safe," he said, "Having cops involved is the second-worst thing that could happen to you."

"What's the first?"

"Having a Colombian hit squad after you."

It was unsettling to hear Diego say these words out loud. It confirmed what she already knew deep down, but she was still convinced this was the job for her.

As Diego was talking, Isabella saw Dominick enter the parking lot through the east entrance. She noted that he was driving a beige Toyota Camry. They both confirmed that no one was following him.

Dominick parked his car four stalls west, in the first row near the area he had entered. He looked in their direction, scanned the parking lot, got out of his car, and walked toward them. Isabella's heart was pounding knowing this was her first encounter with another Cali cartel member.

When Dominick approached, he shook Diego's hand and handed over the keys to his Camry. Diego then introduced Isabella. Dominick greeted her with a sly grin and moved his eyes from head to toe and back up again, checking her out. Her first instinct was to slap him, but she refrained. *What a dirty pervert,* she thought. Diego told Dominick they would return within thirty minutes. Dominick gave a quick nod in agreement and went inside Vons to pass some time.

Diego handed the keys to Isabella and said, "Let's go!"

Isabella asked, "Am I driving?"

"Of course!"

They got in the Camry and exited the parking lot.

"Do you want me to see if we're being followed?"

"Absolutely," Diego replied, "This is when it's important to drive a little crazy."

Isabella started driving toward Diego's auto body shop, about three miles away. She drove the wrong way down a one-way alley. She immediately began laughing at Diego, as he was now the scared one gripping his seat. Diego laughed too. "I'm glad you find this funny!" he said.

Isabella saw no one following, so she made a quick left out of the alley. She then moved into the right-turn only lane and stopped at the red light. She inched forward as if she was making a right turn, but then suddenly veered over and drove straight ahead, running the red light.

People were horrified as she cut them off. She continued straight ahead for about a mile and then got on the freeway, she quickly crossed over all lanes and then back again at a high rate of speed. All the while she was checking her rearview mirror, looking for anyone following her. She saw no one.

Isabella took the next off-ramp and stopped at the red light at the bottom. She saw an opening in the heavy traffic in front of her, so she ran the red light and made a sharp right turn. Several drivers honked their horns as she cut them off. Diego told Isabella she was driving fine but cautioned her, "Do not upset the other drivers to the point they follow you. That would attract the police."

Isabella drove to the auto body shop, still checking the rearview and side mirrors often. She passed the entrance and continued to drive around the block, pulled over to the curb, and watched for anything suspicious. She then drove back to the gate at the entrance.

Diego unlocked and opened the gate, and Isabella made her way to the back. Diego locked the gate behind them, then walked over and unlocked the garage door, pulled it open, and Isabella drove in.

Diego closed and locked the garage door behind them. Once out of the car, he directed Isabella to the back room where the money was.

"Let's do this quickly," Diego said as he pulled up the rug hiding the false floor compartment. He opened it, leaned down, and pulled out two large duffel bags. They were heavy, but Isabella managed to get them into the trunk of Dominick's car with little struggle. Diego closed the false floor and placed the rug back over it. "Time to get back to Dominick," he said.

As they drove out of the parking lot, Isabella looked in her rearview mirror and saw no one behind her. She reassured Diego, "Don't worry. I know this is the time to follow all traffic laws."

Diego chuckled, "Good. We don't want to get pulled over with all this money in the trunk."

"What should I do if we do get pulled over?" Isabella asked.

"This car is not in your name, so you can say you borrowed it from a friend. We would deny knowing anything about the money in the trunk and our friend's whereabouts. The cops will still arrest us and try to get us to admit that the money is ours, but we will be released after forty-eight hours if they can't prove it," Diego said.

Isabella returned to the Vons parking lot and parked in the same spot. Diego then instructed her to give Dominick back his keys and get back to her car. He warned Isabella, "Do not stop and bullshit with Dominick. We don't have time." This wasn't a problem for her because she thought the guy was a creep.

Isabella walked over to Dominick and without saying a word handed him his keys back. Isabella and Diego got back in Isabella's car, and Dominick proceeded to get back in his Camry. Isabella drove out of the parking lot, and Dominick did the same but exited on the other side.

Isabella drove down a couple of alleys and ran a few red lights along the way. Seeing that no one had followed them, she pulled back into the auto body shop.

"You'll hear from me in a couple of days to talk about our next job," Diego said. He got out of Isabella's car and reminded her to be cautious driving home. As she drove out of Diego's sight, she breathed a sigh of relief—her first transaction, her first success.

CHAPTER

10

As Isabella drove back towards her house, she pulled into a small strip mall with a set of pay phones to call Gustavo, the facilitator. She went to the pay phones, pulled the paper with his name and number out from her purse, and dialed his pager. It beeped three times. She entered the number of the pay phone she was on and then hung up.

It was twenty minutes before the phone finally rang. Isabella answered in Spanish.

"Is this Gustavo?" she asked the caller.

"Yes."

"I'm Isabella."

"I have been expecting your call. Meet me at the DMV in Pico Rivera tomorrow morning at ten. I'll get you a new driver's license, and I'll give you a pager. What type of car are you driving, and what color is it?"

"It's a dark blue Honda Civic," she said.

*****

The next morning, Isabella got up at 6:00, showered and got ready, making sure she looked good because she was having her picture taken at the DMV. Using a small Los Angeles County map book, Isabella located the city of Pico Rivera and realized that it was far from her house in the Valley. She knew traffic would be bad, so she left at 7:30 to make sure she had time to find the DMV and get some breakfast.

Isabella got to the DMV at 9:00 and took a quick look at the parking lot. She then continued down the road and found a Mexican restaurant, El Hombre, nearby. She decided it was the perfect place to stop and eat. As she entered, she noticed that most, if not all the other patrons were Mexican and spoke in Spanish, either using a Mexican or South American dialect. She made her way to a table and ordered chorizo and eggs with a cup of coffee.

Immediately, four Mexican men caught her attention. They were staring at her from two tables away. It wasn't long before they began calling lewd comments in her direction, as if she would be interested in them. It was making her angry. She wanted to enjoy her breakfast without being bothered. Diego had warned her about her new occupation and how important it was to not draw attention to herself, so she said nothing to avoid trouble.

Isabella finished her coffee and realized she had twenty minutes to drive down the street and meet Gustavo. She paid her bill and began to walk out. While passing by the table with the Mexican men, one of the them reached out and grazed her butt with his hand. She knew she shouldn't cause a scene, but this time, she couldn't help it. She grabbed a cup of water left on a nearby table, approached the man, and without saying a word, tossed the water directly in his face. He sat there stunned as water dripped off his chin and down the front of his shirt. In the meantime, his friends laughed uncontrollably. She left the restaurant with a smile on her face and sped away without looking back.

Isabella drove to the DMV and found a parking space right away. She remained in her car for about five minutes, when she saw an older Latino with a bushy mustache in the parking lot looking in her direction. Isabella got out of her car as the older Latino made eye contact with her and approached. He asked, "Isabella?"

She replied, "Yes."

"I'm Gustavo. Follow me." Gustavo walked in the DMV and directly to counter number 9. A professional Latina, not much older than Isabella, greeted them. Gustavo introduced Isabella to the woman, but did not give Isabella her name.

The woman spoke in Spanish and handed Isabella a card with the name Maria Herrera on it. "This will be the name you will find on your new driver's license," she said. Isabella looked at Gustavo for reassurance, and he nodded.

The woman then handed Isabella a document to fill out and walked away. Gustavo gave Isabella an address to a PO box to use as her own. He said, "Everything from the DMV will go to this address. I will take care of things as they come."

Isabella had her picture taken and would get her new license in a couple of weeks. In the meantime, the woman told Isabella she could use the temporary one.

Isabella was confused. She looked to Gustavo and said, "Don't I have to take a written exam?" Gustavo smiled and shook his head indicating it was taken care of. He walked Isabella to her car and explained the same things she had already heard from Diego. "If you get pulled over by the police or you need to rent a place for the business, use this new identity and address."

He handed Isabella a pager and said, "From this day forward, members within the organization will be contacting you through this."

Isabella left and drove to a bank of pay phones and paged Diego right away. Five minutes later the phone rang and she answered. She told Diego she had her new driver's license and gave him her new pager number. Diego responded, "Glad it all worked out. By the end of the week, I will be contacting you with some business."

For the next three days, Isabella and her roommate, Juanita, hit the Colombian nightclub scene. Juanita was still working for Laura and Alfredo on one of their lunch trucks. She was curious about Isabella's work and began asking questions, but Isabella responded telling her she was in an import-export business and said no more.

Isabella was fond of Juanita, but didn't know her well enough to trust her about her business dealings. In fact, she didn't know what she was really doing herself. She just knew she wanted to be success-ful in whatever she did.

She and Juanita were both beautiful, young, and loved to dance. Both wanted to meet a Colombian man and have fun like all women their age. While she knew she couldn't get too close to anyone until her business was up and running, it wasn't going to stop her from going out and having a good time.

For three straight nights, Isabella and Juanita dressed in their best and danced until last call at their favorite nightclubs. Every night, men hit on them and wanted to go home with them. Isabella would take phone numbers but nothing more. She even told Juanita that no men were allowed at their townhouse. Right now, she was okay with this arrangement, but deep-down Isabella knew this wouldn't last.

While Isabella realized she would have to deal with this situation soon, for now, she knew she needed to focus on her business. In fact, her first solo transaction was less than twenty-four hours away.

CHAPTER
11

The morning after three nights of clubbing, Isabella was woken by the beeping sound coming from her pager. She recognized the number as Diego's pager. She had to find a pay phone quickly and return his call. She drove away from her complex with caution. She circled her block twice, checking her rearview and side mirrors continuously. She saw no one.

Isabella drove to a Winchell's Donuts where there were several pay phones in the parking lot. She dialed Diego's pager and entered the number of the pay phone she was calling from. She sat on a bench nearby and enjoyed a cup of coffee while she waited. Fifteen minutes passed before the phone rang.

Isabella picked up the receiver and said, "Hello, Diego."

"Someone named Bobby will be paging you within the next few days to arrange a money pick up. You might have to go to Riverside County. It's about seventy miles east of Los Angeles. Once you pick up the money and return, get to a payphone near my auto body shop and page me."

Isabella understood and would let him know what day this was going to happen.

That afternoon, Isabella bought some new clothes and a couple of duffel bags. As she drove home, she drove in her new usual manner when she got close to her townhouse. Isabella saw no one following her, so she parked the car and took her purchases inside.

Thinking ahead, Isabella stuffed the new duffel bags with some of her old clothing. She planned on placing them on top of the duffel bags containing money, just in case she was stopped by the police and her car was searched. *Maybe the cops won't look in all the bags?*

The next morning, Isabella's pager went off at 10:00 with an unfamiliar number. She grabbed the two duffel bags, threw them into the trunk of her car, then headed to the pay phones down the street. She circled her block, looking for anyone who might be following her. She came to a red light, looked both ways for a clearing, ran the red light, and checked her mirrors. Again, she saw no one.

Isabella drove into the Vons parking lot, parked in a stall and waited a few minutes, carefully watching all the activity. Seeing nothing suspicious, she went to the pay phone, called the number in her pager, and a man answered. Speaking in Spanish, the man introduced himself as Bobby. "I have a package for you," he said. He then gave his pager number and told her to drive to the area of the I-215 and Route 60 in Riverside. When she arrived, she needed to get to a payphone and page him.

Isabella had no idea how to get to where the I-215 and Route 60 met. She noticed a bookstore across the parking lot and purchased a Thomas Guide for Los Angeles and Riverside counties. She returned to her car, thumbed through the Thomas Guide and found the route she needed.

*****

When Isabella got to her destination, she spotted a Chevron gas station with a bank of pay phones. She pulled in, called Bobby's pager number, left the pay phone number she was on, and hung up. Bobby called back immediately and gave Isabella directions to a strip mall at the corner of Third Street and Chicago Avenue, just a few blocks away.

"Drive to the strip mall and look for the payphones next to a cigar shop. I will meet you there," Bobby said. Isabella's nerves began to set in. After all, this was going to be her first time picking up money by herself.

As Isabella drove, she checked her mirrors often, always looking out for someone following her. She got to a yellow traffic light, drove through the intersection, and quickly turned into a residential neighborhood. She sped through.

When she arrived at Third and Chicago, she found the pay phones next to the cigar shop. She circled the parking lot twice before entering, then she parked and waited for about five minutes. No one was near the phones, so she pretended to make a call. As she did, she anxiously surveyed the parking lot and again saw no one.

After ten minutes, she noticed a black Toyota Camry enter the parking lot and park at the north end. She noticed a young Latino about her age, wearing jeans and a white button-down shirt, get out of the car.

He approached her and asked, "Are you Isabella?"

"Yes. Bobby?"

He nodded yes, so Isabella gave him her car key and nodded toward her Honda.

Bobby said, "I'll be back in 30 minutes." He then drove away in Isabella's car.

Isabella walked to the north end of the parking lot and entered the 7-Eleven. She took her time as she poured herself a Coke from the self-serve machine. She then spent fifteen minutes browsing through magazines before making her purchase.

She then walked back toward the pay phones and entered a laundromat that overlooked the parking lot. She scouted the lot, saw nothing suspicious, and continued to wait. Bobby should have been back by now, so she was beginning to feel anxious.

Forty-five minutes later, Bobby finally returned. Isabella didn't see anyone following him, so she walked back to the pay phones and again pretended to make a call.

Bobby approached Isabella, handed her the key, gave a quick goodbye, and drove off in his own car.

She took several deep breaths, composed herself, checked her mirrors, and drove back toward the I-215. She entered the freeway and obeyed all traffic laws to avoid being stopped by the police or highway patrol. Isabella's nerves were beginning to get the best of her.

What if Bobby didn't put the money in the trunk of her car? She thought about pulling off the freeway to check but was afraid to be noticed by law enforcement, so she continued on.

It took her two and a half hours to get back to the Valley, thanks to heavy traffic. Once she got off the freeway, she found a pay phone at a Mobil gas station and called Diego's pager. Diego quickly called back and told her to meet him at his auto body shop.

Isabella drove her car directly there, constantly checking her mirrors for anyone following. She passed the shop and made her way around the block as a precaution. Seeing no one, she pulled into the parking lot.

Diego's employee, Miguel, unlocked the gate and then the garage. Isabella pulled in and then he locked the gate and garage door behind her. Diego was there to greet her. He then directed Miguel to go out front and keep an eye on the premises.

Diego asked, "Did you have any problems?"

"As long as the money is here, there is no problem," she answered. She opened the trunk and saw an additional duffel bag, along with the two other bags she had originally placed in there. It was a good sign, but she didn't feel like she was completely out of the woods yet.

Diego pulled Bobby's duffel bag out. "Follow me," Diego said and led her to the same room she had seen before. He placed the bag on a table and opened it. Isabella's heart was pounding. She didn't want anything to go wrong on her first solo pickup.

Diego immediately flashed a wide smile. Isabella looked into the duffel bag herself and heaved a big sigh of relief. As Diego pulled the money out, he told Isabella to set up two tables and grab the money counters. They finished counting it all within a few hours. The grand total was $1.8 million. Just at this moment, Isabella began to realize how much money was sitting right in front of her—something she never thought she'd see in her lifetime.

Diego handed Isabella two thousand dollars as her payment. She was excited—she couldn't believe how easy this was for such a large payment. She took the cash, placed it in one of her duffel bags in the trunk of her car, covered it with clothes, and closed the trunk.

Together they hid the money in the false floor and covered the opening with the rug. Diego looked at Isabella and said, "Good job! I'll be in touch with you in a day or two. You'll pass this package on to the next courier." Diego then called out to Miguel to open the gate.

As Isabella drove off, she started planning a little celebration.

CHAPTER
12

Isabella drove home to her North Hollywood townhouse. She parked in the garage, grabbed the duffel bag containing her money, and carried it into the house. Her roommate, Juanita, was resting on the couch in the living room watching TV. Isabella barely managed a hello and hurried to her room. Juanita attempted to make conversation, but Isabella completely ignored her. She was focused on putting her money away. "I'll be right back," she said and closed her bedroom door behind her.

Isabella locked the door, put the duffel bag on her bed, opened it, and counted her money. *What an amazing day,* she thought. She couldn't wait for another pickup and hoped she could pick up money at least two to three times a month.

Isabella grabbed a couple hundred dollars and put it in her purse. She then placed the bag in the hamper in her closet, put some dirty clothes on top, and closed the closet door.

As Isabella went back to the living room, Juanita looked up and asked, "What's going on? Are you alright?" Isabella apologized and made up an excuse about having to rush to the bathroom.

"How about we get dinner—it's on me," Isabella announced.

"That sounds great," Juanita replied, "Just give me a minute to get ready."

*****

Juanita drove while Isabella directed her to the Scorpion Restaurant and Bar, where she first met Diego. Isabella said, "The food is authentic Colombian and it has a great bar." When they arrived, the restaurant was bustling. A hostess told them it would be a thirty-minute wait, so Isabella left her name and they took a couple of seats at the bar.

While the bartender made their drinks, Isabella and Juanita talked about their day.

Isabella asked, "How are Laura and Alfredo?"

"Oh—they're fine," Juanita replied, "They've got the same routine with the trucks. I mean, I like working there, but I'd like to make more money."

Juanita asked about Isabella's new job and what she did. Isabella, thinking quickly, said she worked for a start-up company that imported and exported small household items. "I like this job—I get to make my own hours, and I enjoy wheeling and dealing with the customers. It's going well, but you never know if things might change."

The bartender returned with their drinks and Isabella changed the subject. A short time later the hostess came and directed them to a booth. Isabella looked at the menu and ordered the most expensive bottle of wine.

Juanita asked, "Can you afford that?"

Isabella laughed, "Don't worry about the price, I get paid very well." They both ordered their food and talked about their plans for the coming weekend.

As they ate, Isabella's pager went off. She glanced at it and recognized the number as a pay phone number Diego used.

"Why do you have a pager? Who's paging you?" Juanita asked.

"It's for work and my boss is calling."

They were almost finished with dinner, so Isabella said she'd call her boss from the pay phones in the parking lot on their way out.

Isabella paid the bill and Juanita thanked her for the wonderful dinner. She added, "I would love to get into your business and make more money!"

Isabella replied, "Maybe someday, but first, I have to learn the ropes myself! Do you mind waiting in the car while I call my boss?"

Isabella walked to the pay phones and returned Diego's call.

Diego said, "Expect a page from a guy named Pedro later tonight. You'll be dropping the money off to him. Tell Pedro to head toward South Gate and page you when he finds a payphone. Get his exact location and drive by to check out the area. If you don't see anything suspicious, then call him back from a different payphone down the street and have him come to your location."

Isabella knew that by working the drop-off this way, she could control the situation and make sure no one was following Pedro. She told Diego she understood and would page him with five ones when she was inbound to his business to pick up the money. "Good," Diego replied and hung up.

When Isabella returned to the car, Juanita asked, "Is everything all right?"

"Yes, but I have to work tonight," Isabella replied.

The drive back to the townhouse was quiet. Isabella could tell Juanita was hurt by her lack of sharing information, but she couldn't risk anything and she had a lot on her mind. They made their way through the front door and Juanita broke the silence. "Do you want me to go with you?"

"No," Isabella responded, "my boss wouldn't like that."

For an hour, both watched TV in silence as Isabella anxiously waited for a page from Pedro. Finally, her pager beeped. She threw on her shoes and a jacket, and said, "I'll be a while. Don't wait up for me." And rushed out the door.

CHAPTER
13

Isabella drove down the street to a set of pay phones and called the number on her pager. A male voice answered in Spanish.

"Are you Pedro?" Isabella asked.

"Yes," replied the voice on the other end.

"Start heading to South Gate and page me when you get there."

About 30 minutes later, she received a page from Pedro. Isabella immediately called him back and asked for his location.

Isabella went to South Gate and drove around the parking lot where Pedro was supposed to be waiting. She observed a lone Latino by the pay phone. She then drove down the street to a set of pay phones in a Ralphs parking lot, paged Pedro, and he called her back. Isabella told him to come to her location to make the switch. Pedro agreed and hung up. Isabella called Diego's pager and entered five ones advising him she'd be at his business soon.

A short time later, a Datsun pickup truck, with a lone Latino driver, pulled into the Ralphs parking lot and drove straight to the pay phones where Isabella was. She saw no one following him.

The driver got out of his small truck and asked, "Are you Isabella?"

"Yes," she said, and Pedro handed over his car key.

Isabella got in the truck, but then quickly got out, slammed the door closed, and walked back to Pedro. She was not happy and let Pedro know it. The truck was a stick shift, and Isabella had never driven one. She tossed Pedro's key back to him and said, "Wait here, I'll be back."

Isabella got into her car, drove out of the parking lot, and headed to Diego's business. As usual, she drove in anti-surveillance mode to be sure no one followed her. When she arrived, Miguel was waiting outside for her and unlocked the gate. Isabella drove into the garage bay as Diego rolled down the garage door and locked it behind her.

Diego was puzzled. "Why are you driving your car?"

Isabella was heated. "Pedro is a fool! He drove up in an old truck, with a stick shift!"

Diego laughed to ease her anger, but deep down he was also mad.

"I'll take care of this later," he said.

Diego put the duffel bag filled with cash into Isabella's trunk, and she headed back to Pedro. As she drove, she obeyed all traffic laws, so she wouldn't attract law enforcement. When she got to where Pedro waited, she circled the parking lot to make sure she didn't see any trouble. She saw none.

Isabella parked her car next to Pedro's truck, got out, and told him to open the hatch to the shell on the back of his truck. Isabella then threw the duffel bag full of money in the bed of his truck. She looked at Pedro with her dark-black eyes and said, "If I ever see this fucking truck again, all deals are off." Isabella got back in her Honda, drove to her townhouse, and called it a night.

For the next year, Isabella continued to make many pickups and drop-offs of money and became very experienced in this portion of the drug trade. She was happy with the money she made and the bosses of the Cali drug cartel took notice of her work.

Isabella didn't want to keep all the money she had earned at her home, but didn't want to put it in a bank account either because it would look suspicious. In order to get around this, she contacted a close childhood friend of hers, Gabriela. She was someone she could trust. Gabriela had dual citizenship in America and Colombia, as she was married to an American. She also worked at a bank in Houston, Texas, and could advise Isabella where to hide her money.

Gabriela suggested that the money could be hidden in a safety deposit box at her bank. "If you're going to carry a lot of cash, you should drive to Houston, not fly," Gabriella said, "If you fly, someone at the airport will likely question you, and they'll probably confiscate it." Isabella agreed to drive to Houston to open up a safety deposit box.

Isabella called Diego and informed him that she'd be out of town for about a week and wouldn't be available to work. Diego said, "That's fine. When you return though, you will continue money drop-offs and pickups, but I'll also begin teaching you the product side of the business." He was referring to cocaine and marijuana. He said he would show her how to set up stash pads; such as homes, apartments, or businesses, to hide product until it was time to distribute it to clients.

Isabella was excited about this because she knew she'd make even more money. But first, she had to hide the drug money she already earned. She drove to Houston with $90,000 in cash and opened up a safety deposit box through Gabriela. Gabriela knew Isabella well enough not to ask where the money came from. As far as Gabriela was concerned, she was helping a customer open a safety deposit box. What the customer put in it was none of her business.

Isabella stayed with Gabriella and her husband and caught up on old times. After a week and a half, she returned to North Hollywood. She was ready to take her business to the next level. Soon, she'd set up her first stash pad. But little did she know that a local police task force was getting closer to the Cali cartel's operation in Southern California.

CHAPTER
14

When I joined the narcotic task force of the Torrance Police Department, our local communities were already experiencing an influx of cocaine and drug dealers. To help law enforcement combat the Colombian drug cartels, the federal government passed legislation, known as asset forfeiture laws, that enabled cities to seize property gathered by their police departments during investigations of drug cartel operations.

These properties included billions of hard cold cash gained from the sale of cocaine and marijuana in the United States, which was intended to be sent back to the drug cartels in Colombia. In addition, cities could also seize the cars, trucks, and houses used by arrested suspects.

From the late 1980s, it seemed as if every police department formed either their own narcotic task force surveillance team, or they joined other cities to form such teams in order to get a share of the profits from seizures. Although many police departments, including the federal Drug Enforcement Agency (DEA), formed task forces, there were only a handful that were really good at combating the drug cartels, making large seizures of drugs and money. The narcotic task force from Torrance was one such agency.

The city of Torrance is in the South Bay area of Los Angeles County. With a population of about 140,000, the city borders the

Pacific Ocean at the southern tip of the Santa Monica Bay between the Palos Verdes Peninsula and the city of Redondo Beach.

The Torrance narcotic task force I worked in was second to none in terms of size and the large amount of money and cocaine seizures we were responsible for. Since there was so much money that could potentially come back to the cities that had narcotic task forces, most cities padded their narcotic task force budgets to give them the resources needed for their clandestine operations. Cities involved in these operations were fine with spending hundreds of thousands of dollars as long as the asset forfeitures brought in more money than went out. For Torrance, the rewards were a hundred-fold.

The one thing that separated Torrance's narcotic task force from the others was its leadership. Torrance's narcotic task force leader was Lt. Steve Pagh. Pagh (pronounced Page) was a man of great intelligence and common sense, a needed combination at the management level. Lieutenant Pagh grew up playing sports and even played minor league professional baseball for some time. He was a catcher, which no doubt gave him the foundation of his leadership.

Lieutenant Pagh's job was to develop two productive teams working in an undercover capacity. First and foremost, he had to choose two mature and competent sergeants to run two undercover teams. One team was a narcotic surveillance team, which during his tenure primarily worked on Colombian drug cartels. The second undercover team was a crime impact team, which surveilled and apprehended career criminals, such as murderers, robbers, rapists, burglars, and child molesters. Basically, this team took down violent predators who preyed upon the good citizens of Torrance and the surrounding communities.

Both teams, although having different functions, assisted each other on cases. So, at times, both teams were supervised by these two undercover supervisors. Lieutenant Pagh knew that the types of cases and individuals surveilled and arrested by the two undercover teams generated a lot of potential liability for himself and the city. He knew it was key to recruit the two most competent and qualified sergeants to run the teams.

Sgt. Dave Tilly was a longtime narcotics expert. He was very intelligent and a real thinker, meaning when you had a conversation with him, you could see his brain working. You could actually see him thinking and analyzing every word you were saying.

Sergeant Tilly was always anticipating his next move. An ultimate chess player would be the best way to describe him. Lieutenant Pagh knew his narcotic sergeant would be working the drug cartels and would need this chess player mentality and, above all, patience. Narcotic cases, especially Colombian drug cartel cases, could take months or even years to conclude before you saw the fruits of your work with arrests, money, and drug seizures.

To head Lieutenant Pagh's other undercover team, the crime impact team, he selected Sergeant Dennis Dalton. Throughout his career, he had a reputation for being a crime-fighter. Lieutenant Pagh selected Sergeant Dalton because the crime impact team dealt with the most violent offenders in society, and with that came a high liability risk. Lieutenant Pagh needed a hands-on leader for this team, the type of leader who was feared but was also respected tremendously.

Lieutenant Pagh was demanding but fair. While his support for his sergeants and their team members was unparalleled, he demanded results. He knew the Colombian drug cartels were infiltrating Southern California with new drug routes and cell networks. He hoped for quick results from Sergeant Tilly and his team.

Sergeant Tilly was allowed to pick his own team members, and he unintentionally selected team members who really didn't know one another well, meaning they hadn't worked as primary partners prior to being selected. All members were proactive police officers that had made a name for themselves while working as uniformed patrol officers.

Sergeant Tilly's narcotic team members were very different from one another. While all had five to fifteen years of experience in law enforcement, the most tenured was the wild one of the group, Denny Carroll. Detective Carroll had a very colorful personality. He was very vocal and funny, and of all the narcotic guys, he needed a little more supervision than the others.

Don't get me wrong, Detective Carroll, like the other members, was very valuable to the team. He was no doubt one of the best, if not the best, surveillance guy on both teams. Being good at surveilling bad guys was essential to the success of both undercover teams. Detective Carroll certainly set a high standard and held us all to that standard.

Both undercover teams were called surveillance teams for a reason; if you couldn't surveil the bad guys without being detected, you were basically useless. Detective Carroll made surveillance fun, especially when he was on point and calling a moving surveillance. A point man on a surveillance had the sole responsibility of communicating the movements of the person being surveilled to the other team members. He did this using his radio mic in his undercover car.

While driving with one hand, he would hold his radio mic with the other out of sight, just below the dashboard. Sometimes the person being surveilled would change directions rapidly, so the detective calling the surveillance had to be good at making decisions quickly.

Whoever called the surveillance had to know where he was, at all times, and know where his other team members were. The point man on a surveillance might have to call a moving surveillance in cars from a block or two out front. Most drug cartel members looked in their rearview mirror for a tail—people following them. They didn't look forward or in the sky for a helicopter. Giving the right direction to other surveillance team members who were paralleling the surveillance from other streets, or even out front or behind by half a mile, was critical to the success of the surveillance.

When Detective Carroll was on point and calling a surveillance, you would need a cheat sheet for the definition of the words he used. For instance, when drug cartel members drove in an anti-surveillance manner to avoid being followed, they might make an abrupt U-turn and drive back the other way. Detective Carroll would call that a whambo.

When we heard "whambo", we knew the chase had turned suddenly, and we had to quickly adjust to maintain surveillance. Eventually, we all followed Detective Carroll's lead and used the same words when on point and calling a surveillance.

The next member on the narcotic team was Bill Mattson. Detective Mattson was a mixture of an altar boy and a college professor. His appearance was deceiving, as he looked innocent. But in reality, he was extremely intelligent, hardworking, and was probably the best investigator. If you were a bad guy, the one detective you didn't want investigating you was Detective Mattson. Not only would he find you, he would also make your life miserable. He was that good!

The third detective on the team was John Sears, whose specialty was working with and on helicopters as an observer. Occasionally the team would use a helicopter to surveil a drug cartel member moving large quantities of cocaine or money. Using a helicopter was expensive, but when the rewards far outweighed the cost, it was a no-brainer. This allowed other team members to stay far out in front, or behind, as they surveilled a moving target.

The fourth member of the team was Detective Jimmy Mack. He was my closest friend on the team and was probably the most well-rounded detective of us all. While the rest of us might have had shortcomings in a particular area; such as in surveillance, on investigations, in case preparations, as a legal expert, in search warrant writing, or as a team player, Mack had it all.

Finally, myself, Detective Tommy Greer—I had been described as the ultimate team player or utility player. I was very good at surveillance, executing search warrants, and dealing with the courts; such as the prosecutors, defense attorneys, and judges. One of my assignments was to take photographs of drug cartel members during our surveillances. I needed to move in close, without detection, to get good photos of the drug cartel members. While this was challenging, it was a lot of fun.

It was the mid-1980s, and police agencies in Southern California had just started to learn how the Colombian drug cartels operated their illegal drug distribution organizations. Sergeant Tilly and our team caught on quickly and started putting unbelievable cases together.

Many cases were developed from prior ones. In some cases, the main drug cartel members we surveilled met up with other drug cartel members within the organization. At the end of a case, if drug cartel members were not arrested and did not flee, future cases developed.

During searches, detectives might find evidence for a future case, or someone we arrested would flip and cooperate to become an informant in order to avoid jail time. These were usually the best cases because informants would continue to work for the drug cartel and put cases together for us. With the help of informants, we seized property, cocaine, and millions of dollars in currency from cocaine sales. We also arrested other members of the drug cartel.

Because the risks to themselves and their families were so high, it was rare that a member of a drug cartel would turn informant. But we would soon catch a break along those lines.

Chapter
15

In many communities, ethnic groups tended to reside in the same area or go to the same churches, restaurants and stores when they arrived in America. The Colombian community was no different. The drug cartels knew this and also knew many Colombians living in the United States through their families back in Colombia. Many Colombians in the United States have respected jobs in banks, schools, government, and other professions. The drug cartels at times would take advantage of these hardworking fellow Colombians.

Gustavo, the facilitator, strong-armed fellow well-established Colombians in the United States and had them rent stash pads in their name. Instead of the actual renter moving in, two low-level members of the drug cartel would reside there and watch the product—cocaine, marijuana—until it was moved to clients. The stash pads were usually in middle-class neighborhoods, where they went unnoticed by neighbors.

Shortly after Isabella returned from Houston, she and Diego met at the Scorpion Restaurant and talked about setting up a stash house to store millions of dollars of cocaine. He explained that his facilitator, Gustavo, rented a house in Encino through a Columbian family. Gustavo paid the husband and wife a couple hundred dollars to fill out the rental application to rent the house.

Diego gave Isabella the address and keys to the house, and told her that in the next week a shipment of cocaine would arrive from

Mexico bound for a warehouse in Orange County. Diego told her he'd get her a driver for a U-Haul truck, and she'd drive this person to pick up the truck. It would be loaded with product, and she'd then take the cocaine and hide it in the Encino stash pad. The driver of the U-Haul along with another mule would stay in the house to guard the cocaine.

"What's to deter these men from stealing the cocaine?" Isabella asked.

"These guys know that if they steal anything, their families back in Colombia will be in danger," Diego replied.

While she didn't have to worry about these two, Diego told Isabella to start building her own network of people she could trust to watch over stash houses and drive trucks to pick up large quantities of cocaine.

*****

Nearly a week later, Isabella received a page from Diego. She used one of the pay phones down the street from her townhouse to contact him.

"A load of cocaine is waiting for you. You need to pick up the truck driver and take him to where the I-405 and I-5 intersect and then let me know when you're in place," Diego explained, "The truck driver's name is Adolfo." He then gave her his pager number and told her to call Adolfo to pick up the shipment.

Isabella paged Adolfo and entered the pay phone number she was calling from. Five minutes later, the phone rang, Isabella answered and introduced herself. The caller confirmed his name was Adolfo.

"Are you ready?" Isabella asked.

"I'll be ready in an hour," Adolfo replied.

"I'll pick you up at the Chevron gas station on Roscoe Boulevard at the 170 Freeway in North Hollywood," Isabella said.

"I'll need at least until noon to get there."

"Okay. Noon it is," she replied.

Isabella returned to her townhouse, showered, and got ready. It was going to be a long day, so she fixed herself something to eat and got back in her car. She drove to the house in Encino and made sure everything was in order. Thanks to light traffic, she arrived in thirty minutes. As she approached the neighborhood, she drove in an anti-surveillance manner to make sure no one was following her. Seeing no one, she drove to the house which was located mid-block of a middle-income neighborhood.

She parked in the driveway. The house had an attached garage, so they could park the U-Haul truck inside to unload the cocaine and not be seen by the neighbors. Using the key Diego had given her, she entered and walked through the house. She noticed the house was clean, but there was no furniture. She found a remote control for the garage on the kitchen counter and opened it. Seeing that it worked, she closed the garage, locked up, and left.

Isabella knew she'd have to buy sleeping bags, pillows, food, and toiletries for Adolfo and the other man who would stay and guard the cocaine. Once they were in place, they weren't allowed to leave, except to answer her pages. Knowing they might be there for months, she'd have to buy them groceries and other items when needed.

Isabella got back into her car and went to pick up Adolfo, arriving at the Chevron gas station a little before noon. As she pulled up to the gas pump and walked into the gas station, she noticed two Latinos standing next to pay phones in the parking lot. She filled her tank and watched them the entire time. The pair appeared to be waiting for someone.

Being cautious, she got back in her car and drove across the street to the pay phones at a Shell gas station, all the while keeping an eye on them. She paged Diego, and he called right back.

"Did you send two couriers?" she asked.

"I'm sorry, but I forgot to tell you that Adolfo was going to bring a second courier. He will drive the truck back to the house with Adolfo and guard the cocaine," he said.

Isabella, being Isabella, was not happy. "From now on, you need to tell me all of the details—you cannot leave anything out!" she exclaimed. She was surprised Diego forgot to tell her this. He was normally overly cautious.

"I understand," he replied, "Have you made contact with either of them yet?"

"When I saw the men, I drove across the street to call you."

Diego chuckled and said, "Man, you are thorough."

Isabella replied, "You were the one who told me to be careful because we are responsible for any problems."

Diego told Isabella he would be more informative going forward. She hung up and drove back across the street, parked her car, and walked to the pay phones where the two Latinos were standing. She entered one of the phone booths, paged Adolfo's pager, and waited to see if one of the Latinos answered.

Sure enough, as the phone rang in Isabella's ear, one of the Latinos reached in his pocket and pulled out his beeping pager. Isabella hung up, exited the phone booth, and greeted Adolfo. Adolfo seemed surprised the person in the next phone booth over was Isabella. He introduced the other Latino as Johnny.

Isabella told Adolfo and Johnny to get in her car, and then she drove to Orange County. A little over two hours later, they arrived where the I-405 and I-5 intersected. She got off the freeway in the city of Lake Forest and quickly found a pay phone in a small strip mall. "You stay here," she commanded and paged Diego for the next step.

Diego called right back and gave her the pager number of the person who would be dropping off the U-Haul truck containing the load of cocaine. Diego told Isabella, "When the person calls you, tell them you are there to pick up the truck. They'll give you directions and instructions."

Isabella hung up, called the pager number Diego had given her, and left the phone number of the pay phone she was at. As she waited for a callback, she leaned into her car and told Adolfo and Johnny what was going on. "We'll wait here until I get a call back," she said. Fifteen minutes later, the phone rang. Isabella answered, "I'm here to pick up the truck." The caller gave her directions to an adjacent city, Mission Viejo, and told Isabella to call him again for further instructions when she arrived there. He then hung up.

Isabella got back into her car and reentered the I-5 and headed south. Soon she saw signs for Mission Viejo. She exited the freeway and drove into the parking lot of an Arco gas station, where she saw some pay phones. She used one of the phones to call her connection and left the number she was calling from.

Isabella's pay phone rang five minutes later, and she answered on the second ring. The caller had the same voice as the man she spoke to earlier. "Are you in Mission Viejo?" the caller asked. When Isabella said yes, he gave her directions to a shopping mall.

"In the parking lot next to mall entrance 3, there's a U-Haul truck parked mid-aisle from the entrance. The truck is unlocked and the keys are underneath the passenger floor mat," the caller said.

"I understand," she replied, "I'm on my way."

Isabella relayed the instructions from the caller to Adolfo and Johnny and told them the shopping mall was just a couple of miles away. She headed towards the mall driving in an anti-surveillance manner, looking for anyone who might be following her. She saw no one.

"Once we get to the U-Haul, the doors will be unlocked. The keys are under the passenger floor mat. Don't look in the back of the truck. Just get in and drive carefully to the freeway," she instructed.

"The truck will have gas in it, so you shouldn't have to stop," she added. She gave them the directions to the stash pad in Encino along with the remote for the garage door. "Drive straight into the garage and close it. I will follow you." Adolfo and Johnny confirmed that they understood.

When Isabella arrived at the shopping mall, she drove around looking for mall entrance 3. On the opposite side of the mall, she saw a U-Haul parked mid-aisle, just as expected. She parked three stalls north of the U-Haul.

Adolfo and Johnny got out of Isabella's car and got into the U-Haul. Adolfo took the driver's side, and Johnny the passenger side. As expected, Adolfo found the key under the passenger side floor mat and then started the engine. He backed out of the parking stall, slowly drove to the nearest exit, and got back on the freeway—heading north on the I-5.

Isabella followed them toward Encino. Because of heavy traffic, it took them four hours to get there. At one point, Adolfo exited the freeway and pulled into a Shell gas station. Isabella watched Johnny get out and run inside. *What is he doing? I asked them not to stop anywhere.* She was not happy. She parked and approached Adolfo who was still in the driver's seat. "What the hell is going on?" she asked.

Adolfo rolled down his window, apologized, and explained that Johnny had to use the restroom. Isabella said nothing and got back in her car. As she did, Johnny came out of the gas station. They quickly got back on the freeway and proceeded to the house in Encino.

As instructed when they arrived, Adolfo opened the garage, pulled straight in, and closed the door behind him. Isabella parked in front, entered the house, and opened the interior door to the garage. She directed them to open the rear door of the U-Haul.

As they did, Isabella noticed a tarp over a large mound in the back. She climbed in and pulled it back. There they found hundreds of kilos of cocaine wrapped in several different colors. Isabella instructed them to unload and count each kilo, then put them all in the middle bedroom closet.

For the next hour, Adolfo and Johnny removed and stacked the kilos neatly in the closet. As they did, Isabella counted each kilo—seven hundred in all. She had Adolfo and Johnny double check the kilos. "If even one kilo is missing after this point, things will not go well for any of us, including me," she warned. Both nodded, acknowledging they understood the consequences. Isabella covered the kilos with the tarp and closed the closet door.

Isabella directed Adolfo to follow her back to a U-Haul facility to return the truck. Johnny was told to stay at the house and guard the cocaine. "After we return the U-Haul, Adolfo and I will do some grocery shopping and get you two some sleeping bags," she said.

After they returned the truck, they drove to a Big 5 Sporting Goods and bought sleeping bags, pillows, and a small portable camping table to eat on. Isabella and Adolfo then purchased a week's worth of groceries at a local grocery store.

As they drove back to the stash house, Isabella ran a few red traffic lights, quickly changed lanes, and looked in her rearview mirror.

Adolfo looked like he was going to have a heart attack. "Relax," she smiled, "I'm just making sure no one is following us."

When they returned to the neighborhood, she drove around the block a few times, conducting her own countersurveillance. She checked for anyone who might be staking out the stash pad. She saw no one. She returned to the house, parked in front, and entered using the front door. Johnny came out to help Adolfo carry in their purchases.

Isabella went straight to the bedroom and counted the kilos in the closet again and found all seven hundred were still there. Knowing that the street value of seven hundred kilos was around $70 million, she wasn't going to take any chances with even one kilo being tampered with. "I'm leaving now. Don't either of you answer the door for any reason," she said. "I'll page you with the number seven when I come back."

Isabella left and drove straight to a pay phone down the street. She paged Diego to let him know that everything was in place and secure. "I counted seven hundred kilos and had Adolfo and Johnny do the same," she said.

"Thank you for being so thorough. Meet me tomorrow morning at ten. I'll be at the Denny's down the street from your townhouse," Diego said. "At that time, I will explain what our next move will be." It was now 11:00 p.m. and Isabella was exhausted. She drove home and went straight to bed.

The following morning, they met at Denny's. Isabella found Diego in a booth at the back of the restaurant. After the waitress took their orders, Isabella said, "Aside from the surprise of two contacts showing up yesterday, everything went smoothly."

"In the future, I'll check out the house, buy groceries, and get some furniture and bedding before dropping off the load of cocaine. It was too stressful to run around after the drop off," she said. Diego nodded in agreement. "Next time, I hope to have my own people working for me. I should be able to trust them to do little things like that," she said.

Diego replied, "Yes, but that will take time. I will contact you in a few days— I will have a customer for you soon. You'll be dropping off some kilos to him."

"How many?" Isabella asked.

"I'll let you know when I contact you."

After they finished breakfast and returned to their cars, Diego cautioned Isabella to be very careful and use her gut feeling when she dropped off kilos to a client. "It's the deadliest part of the job," he said. He reiterated the things that could go wrong, "Someone might be setting you up and rip off the kilos, or worse, the police could arrest you with the kilos in your car and send you to prison for a long time." Diego reminded her to use all the driving techniques and caution she had learned these past years. "Don't worry, I will," she assured him. In a week, Isabella would discover the challenge of the "deadliest part of the job" for the first time.

CHAPTER
16

Four days passed before Isabella received a page from Diego. When she contacted him, he told her to expect a page from a client in the next day or two. "You'll drop off two hundred kilos," he said.

The next day, Isabella received a page. She drove down the street from her townhouse to call back from a pay phone. The person on the other end said that his name was Juan and he was directed to pick up two hundred kilos of cocaine. Isabella told Juan to head to the area where the I-405 and US 101 connect and page her back.

"How long will it take you to get there?" she asked.

"About two hours," he replied.

Isabella looked at her watch. It was 9:30 a.m., but she wanted to wait until traffic was heavier to better hide a drop-off. She told Juan to page her around 3:00 p.m. Juan agreed and hung up. She picked the I-405 and US 101 because it was far enough away, but close enough to the stash house.

Isabella drove to the area to choose a parking lot for the drop-off. This way, when Juan called, she could tell him where to go. She found an Albertsons with a medium-sized parking lot near the intersection of the two freeways. She liked this location because she knew that at around 4:00 p.m., the parking lot would be full, and she would go unnoticed. She then drove back to her townhouse to make breakfast and waited.

Around 2:00 p.m., Isabella drove to the Albertsons's parking lot. It only took her about twenty minutes to get there. She drove around the lot looking for some pay phones and noticed two sets right in front of the store. Isabella had thirty minutes to spare, so she drove to a nearby McDonald's and grabbed a bite to eat.

She finished eating at 3:00 p.m., but still hadn't heard from Juan. She decided to drive back toward Albertsons, but this time, parked across the street in a small strip mall where she had a view of the pay phones. Finally, at 3:30 p.m., she received a page from Juan. She immediately used a pay phone to call him back.

Juan answered and said he was in the area of the I-405 and US 101. Isabella gave him directions to the parking lot. "Use the pay phones in front of Albertson's and page me when you get there," she said. "What kind of car are you driving? What color?"

"A dark blue Toyota Camry," he replied.

"Okay, I'll be waiting for your call."

A short time later, a dark blue Toyota Camry entered the parking lot and parked in the north end of the lot. Isabella watched a dark-skinned Latino exit the Camry and walk to the pay phones in front of the store. A minute later, she received a page and called Juan back.

"I'm at Albertsons," he said.

"Okay—hang tight, I'll be there in fifteen minutes," she replied.

She returned to her car and kept an eye on him. Isabella didn't see any red flags to indicate he'd been followed or that he was working for the police.

Isabella started her car and drove over to the area where Juan had parked. She got out of her car, walked to the pay phones where he was standing, and paged Adolfo to let him know she was on the way. She then told Juan to hand over his keys. "I'll be back in thirty minutes," she said and drove off.

As Isabella got closer to the stash house, she began to drive in an anti-surveillance manner to detect anyone following her. At several intersections she drove into left-turn-only lanes, but instead of turning left when the traffic light turned green, she drove straight ahead.

She ran a couple of red lights, again looking in her rearview mirror for someone following her. The coast was clear.

When she got to the stash house, Isabella drove around the block twice, pulled over to the curb, and looked around. She saw no one. Isabella knew it was critical to be cautious because she didn't know if anyone had followed Juan. Her heart was pounding. She loved the adrenaline high, but she was scared at the same time. She didn't trust anyone.

When Isabella was sure no one was following her, she used the remote to open the garage to the stash house, drove in, and closed the door behind her. As she got out of the car, Adolfo and Johnny were waiting for her at the door to the house inside the garage. "Get the containers I brought over earlier, and put one hundred kilos in each," she directed.

Isabella followed them to the closet where the kilos of cocaine were stored and closely watched Adolfo and Johnny as they filled the containers. As the kilos were placed inside, she counted them and then counted the remaining ones in the closet to make sure all was accounted for.

Isabella then told them to place the containers in the trunk of the Toyota Camry. The containers barely fit inside the trunk and the back end of the car was noticeably weighted down. She was worried, but knew it would have to do.

"I'm heading out—do you two need anything?" she asked.

"Could we get a TV or at least a radio?" asked Adolfo.

"I'll see what I can do."

Isabella drove back to Albertsons where she found Juan still standing in front of the pay phones. She surveyed the parking lot and didn't notice anything unusual. She parked the car in the same spot, got out, and handed Juan his keys. She quickly said goodbye, got back in her car, took a deep breath, and drove out of the parking lot.

Since it was only 6:00 p.m., she drove to a Best Buy on the way back to the house. There she selected a portable Sony stereo system with portable speakers to reward Adolfo and Johnny for their work.

Isabella paid for the stereo using cash, then drove to a pay phone and paged Adolfo to let him know she was returning. On the way back, she stopped at a Mexican fast-food restaurant and bought Adolfo and Johnny dinner—ordering plenty for leftovers.

She drove around the neighborhood looking for anything out of the ordinary. Seeing nothing, she pulled into the garage and closed the door behind her. Adolfo was standing at the door with a smile on his face. "How'd it go?" he asked.

"Just fine," she answered. "I want to thank you for taking care of everything. I've brought you dinner, and you'll find something to keep you entertained in the backseat of my car."

Johnny now appeared beside Adolfo with a smile on his face because he could smell the food. She walked in the house and headed straight to the closet where the remaining kilos of cocaine were stored.

Isabella then recounted the remaining five hundred kilos. She didn't hide the fact that she was counting them each time she came to the house because she wanted them to know she was checking up on them. "I'll talk to my boss and find out when the next drop-off is. When I do, I'll page you with the number seven again, so you'll know I'm coming for more." Adolfo confirmed he understood, and Isabella left them to guard the stash.

Isabella was tired, but she had to let Diego know that the drop-off was successful. She headed back toward her townhouse and stopped at the same pay phones down the street to page him. Within fifteen minutes, Diego called back. "Everything went smoothly—I gave Juan the two hundred kilos and confirmed the other five hundred are secure," she said.

"Thank you. As soon as I hear from my bosses, I'll let you know when the next drop off will be," he said.

"Good," she replied, "I'm exhausted—I'm going home to get some sleep." She hung up and drove back to her townhouse.

When Isabella walked in, she found Juanita doing dishes. "Where have you been?" she asked.

"I've been at work," Isabella responded.

Juanita got nosy and began asking her questions about her job. But Isabella immediately cut her off. "I was with clients. Doing business," she said sternly. "I really don't want to talk about it."

CAPT. BRADLEY T. WILSON

Seeing Juanita was not satisfied with her response, she hugged her. "Please don't worry," she said in a softer tone.

Juanita, feeling a little reassured, responded with a half-smile as Isabella grabbed a beer from the refrigerator and sat down to watch a little TV.

For the next month and a half, Isabella did four more drop-offs of cocaine to clients. The most product she dropped off at one given time was 150 kilos. With only 100 kilos left, she waited for her next and final drop-off.

CHAPTER
17

One night, around 6:30 p.m., while Isabella and Juanita were out having dinner, Isabella's pager went off. She didn't recognize the number which wasn't unusual. Isabella had not been in the business long, and there were so many clients throughout Southern California she hadn't worked with. In the beginning, Diego would let her know when a client would page her but toward the end of this 700-kilo load, he didn't. Diego only needed a confirmation call from Isabella, and to know how many kilos she passed on and to who.

Diego would then forward this information to the bosses in Colombia. Like any other business, the Cali cartel drug enterprise supplied the product and received payment for their product. The cash was then laundered back to Colombia.

Isabella said to Juanita, "Excuse me a moment, I've got to return this page." She used a pay phone near the restrooms in the restaurant and returned the call. A Latino man answered asking for 200 kilos of cocaine.

"I can get you one hundred," she replied.

"No, no," he insisted, "I need two hundred—one hundred is not enough." Isabella thought this was odd—this was the first time a client had insisted that she give him more than what she offered. Asking for more was one thing, but insisting in this manner was a red flag to her. When Isabella was about to cut this guy off and hang up, the caller backed down and agreed to take the 100.

The caller then said he needed it tonight. "That's not possible—I'm busy tonight. We can do it tomorrow," Isabella said.

But the caller was persistent and explained, "I'm going back to Colombia tomorrow, so I have to get this done tonight."

Isabella hadn't experienced this kind of pushiness before, and she was bothered by the caller dictating this transaction. She finally conceded and told him to drive to the area where the I-405 and US 101 intersected, then call her. The caller agreed and said his name was Augie. She asked how long it would take him to get there. "About an hour and a half," he replied. Isabella then hung up the phone.

Isabella and Juanita were planning on going clubbing later—she knew Juanita wouldn't be happy that she was canceling their plans, but she wanted to get rid of the last 100 kilos of cocaine she had at the stash pad. When she returned to the table, she gave Juanita an explanation and apologized, and then told her she had to cancel their plans for the night.

Isabella saw the disappointment on Juanita's face and could hear it in her voice, so she gave in to a compromise. "Okay, let's finish our dinner and go to the club. I'm supposed to get a page around 8:30. I'll leave to do my business and then come back. I should be finished around 10:00— just when things start getting fun," she said.

"Can I come with you? I'd rather not be at the club alone," Juanita said.

"No, no, that can't happen," Isabella replied.

Immediately, Juanita began to cry. She reached out and placed her hands on each side of Isabella's cheeks, pulling her face close to hers while looking straight in her eyes. Her voice quivered as she said, "Isabella, you can tell me—are you a prostitute?"

Isabella started to laugh, but could read the anguish on Juanita's face and held back. Isabella could see how she came to this conclusion. Every time she told Juanita she was going to meet a client, the client was a male. Each time she met a client, it was for no more than a couple of hours and happened at all times of the day and night. Isabella grabbed Juanita's hand and tried to reassure her. "No, Juanita, I promise you, I'm not a prostitute," she said.

While Isabella knew she could trust Juanita with her secret, she wasn't quite ready to do so right then at the restaurant. "After tonight, I'll explain everything to you, but it's not a good time right now."

This made Juanita smile. "I'm sorry, I hope you understand."

Isabella smiled back. "Yes, of course I do. I understand and I love you for being concerned."

"So, you promise you'll tell me all about your business tomorrow?"

Isabella agreed and changed the subject. "Let's go dancing!"

It was 8:00 p.m. when Isabella and Juanita arrived at one of their favorite Latino clubs. Although a little early, they went in anyway. Right away, they met up with some friends that they had met there a year prior. There were three women and two men, and all were from the same area of Colombia as Isabella and Juanita. Everyone ordered drinks except Isabella. "I'm waiting for a business call, and I'll have to leave soon," she explained.

At 8:30 p.m., Isabella received a page. She left the club and stepped outside to return the call from a pay phone adjacent to the front door. Augie answered and let her know he was in the area. Isabella was in Sherman Oaks, just a short drive to where he was. Wanting to get back to the club, she gave Augie directions to the pay phones in front of Albertsons, just down the street from where he was calling.

"Park in the Albertsons's lot and page me from one of the pay phones in front of the grocery store," she instructed. She was careless because she was in a hurry. Normally, she would go to the location first and then give directions, so she could watch the client drive into the parking lot and see if anyone was following them.

Isabella asked, "What color is your shirt?"

"I'm wearing a blue shirt," he answered. "I'll be there in ten minutes, and I'll page you when I arrive."

Exactly ten minutes later, Isabella received a page from the pay phone outside Albertsons. Instead of parking across the street and watching Augie in the parking lot, she drove directly into the

Albertsons's parking lot and parked her Honda in a stall right in front of the pay phones.

Isabella saw a heavyset Latino in a blue shirt standing next to the pay phones. She got out of her car and asked if he was Augie. "Yes, I am," he said. She then used a pay phone to page Adolfo and let him know she'd be there shortly to pick up the remaining 100 kilos.

Isabella noticed that Augie was acting unusual. "Are you okay? Is anything wrong? You seem nervous," she remarked.

"I'm always nervous when I do a pick up," he replied.

Isabella started to get a bad feeling. She knew how it felt to be jumpy when conducting this kind of business, but Augie seemed a little more nervous than most clients. He was sweating and stuttering. Although Isabella noticed these red flags, she didn't listen to her intuition because she was in a hurry to get back to her friends.

"Give me your car key," she said. "Where are you parked?"

Augie gave Isabella his key and pointed to the car parked right next to hers. "It's the van," he said.

"Wait here. I'll be back in thirty minutes," she said.

She then got into his van and looked around to see if anyone was watching her. Seeing no one, she slowly backed out of the parking stall and drove out of the parking lot.

When she approached the first busy intersection, Isabella drove into the left-turn lane and inched out against the red traffic light. When it was clear, she ran the light to see if anyone was following her. Her heart sank. She looked in her review mirror and saw two cars run the same light. She couldn't believe it! Now, she was scared. She cursed herself for taking shortcuts and not aborting when she had seen so many warning signs. The worst part was, she had let Augie dictate this from the onset.

She promised herself that if she got out of this jam, she'd never let this kind of thing happen again. Isabella took a deep breath and tried to relax. Thoughts were racing through her head. *Who was following her? Was it law enforcement or other drug traffickers trying to rip her off? If it was the police, they had nothing on her.* She decided she wasn't going to go to the stash pad. Instead, she planned to take her followers on a wild ride.

She came to another red traffic light and again got in the left-turn-only lane. She ran the red light and made a quick U-turn. As she did, she looked over into the two cars she believed were following her. Both cars had a gringo behind the wheel. Both drivers looked straight ahead and avoided eye contact with her.

Isabella began to drive at a high rate of speed while looking in her rearview mirror. When she was two blocks ahead, she saw both cars make U-turns and then proceed to drive back toward her. She made a sharp right turn and drove as fast as Augie's van would go. She quickly entered the I-405 on-ramp heading southbound, using the shoulder lane to pass cars waiting at the meter light at the top of the on-ramp. Traffic was very heavy, so she continued to use the shoulder lane until she came to the next exit. She took the off-ramp, ran a red traffic light at the bottom, and turned left. She glanced in her review mirror and saw no one following her.

Isabella couldn't be sure she'd lost her pursuers, so she drove to Sherman Oaks Mall. She parked the van in a crowded area, got out, and walked as fast as she could into the mall. She wanted to turn back and look out the mall entrance to see if anyone was following her, but she was too scared. She looked straight ahead and kept walking.

Isabella walked to the AMC Theaters, bought a ticket for a movie, entered the theater, and sat near the exit so she could keep an eye on who came in and out. About an hour later, she finally felt safe enough to make a call at a pay phone in the lobby. She paged Diego adding the numbers 911.

Within 10 minutes, the pay phone rang. The lobby was quiet, and the ring of the phone made Isabella jump. She whispered as she told Diego what had happened.

"Are you sure they were following you?" Diego asked.

"I'm positive. No one was following me until I left Augie," she said. "I was at dinner with my roommate. After that, we met some friends at a nightclub. I'm certain I wasn't being followed then."

She then explained how pushy Augie had been. How he insisted on doing the exchange tonight because he was going back to

Colombia tomorrow. She also described Augie's demeanor; his sweating and stuttering. "I'm positive no one followed me to the pickup site either. It was only after I met Augie and took his van," she said.

"Do you want me to come pick you up?" he asked.

"I'm alright now. I'll find a ride," she said.

"Don't go back to your car tonight. We'll look for it tomorrow," Diego said. "If law enforcement was following you, they'll impound your car by tomorrow. I'll go by Albertson's in the morning and see if it's still there. If it's not, we know this Augie guy is working with the cops, and he'll pay. I'll let the bosses know about everything."

It was now 11:30 p.m., and Isabella knew Juanita would be worried about her. She wasn't sure if she should call the club and have Juanita paged over the intercom, or if she should just get a taxi and go to the club herself. Isabella thought the latter would be better and less worrisome for Juanita. She called a cab and returned to the dance club in Sherman Oaks.

It was nearly midnight when Isabella was dropped off. She still had the stamp on her wrist from earlier, so she got back in for free. She entered and saw Juanita dancing with a circle of friends. She walked straight over and joined in on the fun. Juanita hugged her and said, "I've been so worried! Where have you been? What happened?"

Isabella replied, "I'll explain everything tomorrow. I promise." Juanita nodded and they enjoyed the rest of the evening.

At 2:00 a.m., they walked out of the club to go home and Isabella realized she had no car. Juanita asked, "Where's your car?"

Isabella looked at her and said, "I don't have it."

Juanita stared quizzically and asked, "What's going on?"

Isabella noticed their other friends were now listening to their conversation. She turned back to Juanita and explained, "My car was stolen earlier. That's why it took me so long to get back to the club. I'll get a cab." She returned to the club and asked an employee to call them a taxi.

When they got home, Juanita threw her coat and purse down, "What the hell is going on Isabella?" She looked at Isabella. "I've known you for a long time and I know when you're lying. I know you've been lying to me about your job. You're lying to me about your car. I want to know the truth right now."

Isabella plopped on the couch and said, "Sit down. This is going to take a while." Juanita nodded, but was now nervous about what she was going to hear.

Isabella told Juanita everything. Juanita exclaimed, "I don't believe it. You can't be involved in the drug business. I would have seen the signs. I would have known."

"No, you wouldn't. It's not like I'm selling drugs from the house." Isabella explained that she was involved in an enterprise, which was run like a business.

She got up from the couch. "Come with me," Isabella said. She led Juanita to her room, pulled the duffel bag out of her closet, put it on her bed, and opened it.

Juanita gasped, "How much is there?"

"$120,000."

"Who does this money belong to?" Juanita asked.

Isabella looked at her. "This money is mine. It's mine for doing my part in the business. Remember when I went to visit my friend Gabriela in Houston? She helped me open a safety deposit box to hide even more money. I need to bring this to Houston too."

"Aren't you scared of being caught or hurt?"

"I wasn't—until tonight, when I was followed." She shook her head and said, "I've never been so scared in my life. I definitely made some mistakes—I should've done things differently—been more careful—but I was in a hurry and almost got caught by the police."

"How did you know it was the police?"

Isabella replied, "I got a good look at them and they were both gringos. I'm sure they were the police. Tomorrow, my boss is going back to the parking lot where I left my car. If it's gone, then I'll know for sure." She looked at Juanita and said, "I hope you're not angry with me."

"I'm not mad, but I'm worried that something might happen to you."

Isabella replied, "Soon I'll be in the position to have other people work for me. That'll make it a lot harder for me to get caught. "Let's get some sleep, and we can talk more about it in the morning."

As she walked out of Isabella's bedroom, Juanita asked, "Does anyone else know? Laura, Alfredo, Gabriela—anyone?"

"Gabriela knows a little bit, but no one else."

After Juanita went to bed, Isabella realized she actually felt relieved that Juanita finally knew the truth. Tomorrow would be an interesting day. She needed to find out about her car, and she had to go to the stash house and see if Adolfo and Johnny were okay. Deep down she knew they'd be fine because she didn't go there, but she was anxious anyway. What if the police were aware of the stash pad and knew what was in it? She'd be arrested and sent to prison for sure.

She was still angry with Augie for setting her up, and she wanted him to pay. She was tired and her head hurt thinking about the events of the evening, so she fell asleep quickly.

CHAPTER
18

I sabella was awakened by her pager the next morning. She didn't recognize the number, but thought it might be Diego calling about her car. She quickly threw on some sweats and went into the living room to look for Juanita's car keys. She was just leaving when Juanita surprised her.

"What's the rush—are you OK? Where are you going?" she asked.

"I just got paged and I need to call them back. I think it's my boss. Can I borrow your car?"

Juanita asked, "Why not use the house phone?"

"I can't because the police will be able to connect me to the drug cartel. I have to use a pay phone."

Juanita smiled and said, "You know better than me. Yes, take my car."

Isabella smiled back. "I'll be back soon. This shouldn't take long."

Isabella drove cautiously to the pay phones down the street. She didn't drive erratically, but closely watched the drivers around her. When she got to her regular pay phones, she noticed someone using one. While not unusual, she was a bit nervous. She decided that it was time to switch things up for a while and use different meeting locations and pay phones.

She drove about a mile before she found a new pay phone. She then called the number she received on her pager.

Diego answered right away. "How are you?"

"I'm a little shaken up and starting to feel paranoid, which is probably a good thing. Have you checked on my car?"

"I'm across the street from Albertsons now. Your car is gone."

Her heart sank. "Do you think it's the police?"

"Yes, I'm positive it was the police. You were set up by Augie. I'll need to let David know what happened. In the meantime, you need to change your normal routine, so they can't continue to track you."

"Yes, I've already started to do things differently."

Isabella asked Diego what she should do about a car since hers was impounded. "I'll pick you up in an hour and take you to my shop. You can use one of mine. I've already contacted Gustavo, the facilitator, and told him what happened. He told me that he picked up mail from the PO box two days ago without any problems, but he'd get a new PO box because your car was registered there."

"Is there any paperwork from the house rental that went to the PO box?" she asked.

"No, Gustavo uses a different PO box address for that, and he paid six months' rent up front in cash."

"I need to get to the house and remove the 100 kilos and tell Adolfo and Johnny what happened. I need to get them out of there," she said. Diego agreed, but he didn't care about Adolfo or Johnny. He just wanted the kilos.

Diego said, "After you get the car, I will need you to get the remaining kilos and bring them to me. Be very careful. The police may be watching the house." Her stomach ached at the thought of this—she knew she had no choice but to go there.

"I'll see you in an hour," he said and then ended the phone call.

Isabella drove Juanita's car home. She drove around her block several times and kept an eye out for anyone who might be following her. When she felt it was safe, she returned home. As she walked in, Juanita asked, "Did your boss call?"

"Yes," she said, "He's picking me up in an hour to get me a new car because the police had taken mine."

"Now I'm worried, Isabella. The police probably know where we live because they have your car," Juanita exclaimed.

Isabella tried to calm her nerves. "The car isn't registered to our townhouse or even in my name. There is no way they can make a connection."

It was 11:00 a.m. when Diego arrived to pick up Isabella. "I won't be home until this evening," she called out to Juanita. Diego drove her to his business in South Gate. They both watched for anyone who might be following them. It was all clear.

When they arrived, Miguel unlocked the gate. Diego drove to the back, pulled into the garage, and Miguel closed the garage's roll-up door behind them.

Diego said, "Miguel, go get the gray Toyota Camry. Isabella will be using it from now on."

Isabella asked, "Who does the car belong to?"

"The car belongs to the organization and it's registered to a house in the city of Monrovia. A Columbian couple lives there— we pay them well to let us register cars there. They don't ask any questions."

Isabella said, "I don't want to, but I'll go to the stash house to get the rest of the kilos now."

"I've been thinking about that," Diego said, "I think the house is safe. If the police knew about the cocaine, they would've already gone in and confiscated it, and Adolfo and Johnny would've been arrested by now. But, the only way to find out for sure, is to go there. You must be extremely cautious. You must drive around the neighborhood for a while before going in. If everything checks out, it's okay to leave the cocaine there until we find another buyer."

Isabella agreed and told him she'd page him after she checked out the house. She said, "If you don't hear from me within two hours, then I've probably been arrested. You make sure this Augie guy pays for putting me through this."

Diego assured her it was already being addressed by the bosses in Colombia.

Isabella drove towards the house and used a pay phone along the way to page Adolfo. Then she surveilled the neighborhood and verified that no one was watching the house. She felt like throwing up—she was terrified. She opened the garage, pulled in, and closed the door behind her. There wasn't any sign of Adolfo or Johnny. Now she was really scared, but she had no choice but to enter.

When she got in, she heard the radio blaring and saw Adolfo and Johnny playing cards. She was both relieved and angry. "Why didn't you meet me at the door?" she demanded.

Adolfo said, "I didn't hear my pager."

"Turn that radio down so you can hear your pager next time."

"Why did you page us last night? You never showed up," Adolfo asked.

She decided not to tell them what had happened because they might leave. "Sorry about that—I got sidetracked with some other business. Do you guys need anything? Is there anything I can get for you?" she asked. Both said no. As usual, she then went into the bedroom, counted the kilos of cocaine and was relieved to see that they were all there. "I hope to have a buyer for the last 100 kilos soon," she said.

Isabella left and immediately drove to a pay phone to page Diego. He called back within 10 minutes. "It's all good," she said. "Obviously, the police are not aware of the stash house." Diego was happy the remaining 100 kilos of cocaine were safe.

"I hope we hear about the last drop-off soon," he said. "If a client contacts you before me, let me know right away." Isabella agreed.

As she drove home, Isabella received a page from an unknown number. She had a feeling it was a client, but she wasn't sure if she wanted to start back up again so soon. She still felt anxious, but also knew she had to continue to conduct business, so she would get paid.

When she arrived in Van Nuys, she pulled into a small strip mall parking lot that had pay phones. She called the number, and as usual, a male Latino voice answered. He said he was calling to pick up some property. She told the caller she had 100 kilos for him. "Drive to Van Nuys and page me when you arrive. How long will it take you to get here?" she asked.

"Three hours," he replied.

"I'll see you soon."

Isabella liked Van Nuys for drop-offs because it was a city busy with traffic, people, and businesses. Isabella found a perfect location just off Van Nuys Boulevard, near the mall—close to the I-405 and the stash house. On the corner was the Van Nuys mall, which had a bank of pay phones and a large parking lot full of cars. Isabella wrote down the address to give to the client when he called her back.

Since she was at the mall, Isabella decided to do a little shopping. She then had a late lunch and at 3:30 p.m., she received a page. She drove to a strip mall across the street from the pay phones where she was going to send the client. She told herself she'd call the shots about when and where to drop off the cocaine. She'd also be able to see this client drive into the parking lot and see if anyone came in with him.

Isabella called the number on her pager. The same Latino voice answered and said he was in the area.

"What color and type of car are you driving? What are you wearing?" she asked.

"I'm driving a black Ford Fiesta and I'm wearing a long-sleeved green plaid shirt."

Isabella gave him the address and told him to page her from that location. He told her his name was Antonio and he understood where to go.

Fifteen minutes later, she saw a Latino in a black Ford Fiesta pull into the mall parking lot. She noted another car behind him. This alarmed Isabella. She wasn't going to be fooled again. She kept an eye on Antonio and the car following behind. They parked near each other. Her worry intensified until she saw the car door open and an elderly black woman got out with a small child.

She continued to watch Antonio closely. He walked up to the pay phones and made a call. Isabella received a page immediately. She waited 15 more minutes before driving to a pay phone to return the call. When she was sure he was alone, she paged Adolfo at the stash house to let him know she was on her way.

She then drove to Antonio and parked her car a couple of rows over from his. She approached the bank of phones where Antonio was standing and called the number he had called from. The phone rang next to her and Antonio answered. Isabella was all business and asked for his key while they were still on the phones. She hung up, took the key, then got in his car and left the parking lot.

As she drove away, Isabella passed an LAPD police car entering the parking lot. Her heart raced. She wasn't going to take any chances, so she decided to drive across the street and watch it carefully. For 10 minutes the police car slowly made its way around the mall and finally out of sight. Isabella let out a sigh of relief, and sped off.

Isabella drove erratically, constantly looking in her review mirror to see if she was being followed. She approached the I-405 on-ramp and entered. She merged onto the freeway and quickly changed lanes. She crossed all the way over to the fast lane, then quickly back to the slow lane and exited the next off-ramp. No one was following her.

At the bottom of the off-ramp, she made sure the traffic was clear, then ran a red traffic light. Still, no one followed her. Isabella continued toward the stash house, entered the neighborhood and drove around the block several times. After she pulled over to make sure no one was following her, she drove into the garage and closed the garage door behind her. Adolfo appeared and asked Isabella how many kilos. "All 100 of them," she replied.

Isabella and Adolfo counted all 100 kilos of cocaine. Adolfo and Johnny put them into a container and placed it into the trunk of the Ford Fiesta. "After I drop this load off," Isabella said, "I'll come back and get you. You'll have some time off until we get another load in." They smiled and thanked her.

Isabella drove straight back to the Van Nuys mall, checking constantly to make sure she wasn't being followed. When she arrived at the parking lot, Antonio made eye contact with her as she drove by him. The lot was full. She parked Antonio's Ford Fiesta three aisles down from where she had picked it up. He walked over to Isabella, and she handed him his keys. She didn't say a word to him; just got back in her own car and left.

She drove a mile then pulled over to a set of pay phones to page Diego. He called back within 10 minutes. "Everything went smooth-ly—I dropped off the remaining 100 kilos to this guy, Antonio. I'm heading back to pick up Adolfo and Johnny. I'll drop them off where I first picked them up. Am I supposed to pay them?" she asked.

"No, you don't have to worry about that—I'll take care of it. I'll get back to you soon and pay you as well."

Isabella paged Adolfo to let him know she was on her way. She was relieved that there was no more cocaine left. When she got back to the house to pick up Adolfo and Johnny, they greeted her with big smiles. They couldn't wait to get out of there.

Isabella dropped them off at the Chevron gas station at Roscoe Boulevard. "Thank you. More than likely, I'll see you again," she said.

Isabella returned home and found Juanita cooking dinner. While they ate, Juanita asked, "What do you think? Can I work with you?"

Isabella pondered before replying, "I'll be able to hire you when I move up in the organization. In the meantime, you'll have to continue working for Laura and Alfredo. Right now, it's too dangerous for you to do what I'm doing."

Disappointed, Juanita said, "I understand."

"I'll cover your living expenses until I find a position for you," Isabella offered. She didn't want to hurt her feelings, but she felt Juanita was way too naive to do what she was doing.

It was the mid-1980's and the climate regarding the smuggling of cocaine from Colombia into the United States had changed. The United States government was cracking down on cocaine and money laundering in Miami and New York.

This crackdown on the east coast caused the Cali Drug Cartel to change up their drug routes into the United States. For the most part, the Cali Drug Cartel started flying large shipments of cocaine from Colombia into private landing strips in Mexico. From there, the Cali Drug Cartel negotiated and paid the Mexicans to transport the cocaine in large semitrucks through the borders of Texas, Arizona, and California. Once the cocaine safely arrived in the United States, the Colombians would take back possession; transporting and distributing the cocaine throughout the states.

89

Thanks to this new drug route, Isabella was busier than ever. But she wasn't complaining—she was making a lot of money. She finally hired Juanita to take her money to Houston and put it in one of several safety deposit boxes. Soon, however, a drastic change would make an impact on her business.

CHAPTER
19

One day, Isabella received a page from someone back in Colombia. She had no idea who it might be. She paged Diego to see if he knew who it was, but after waiting an hour, he still hadn't called her back. When she called the number from Colombia, she discovered that it was Diego's boss, David. David congratulated Isabella for her great work and told her that the bosses kept track of all their couriers, like her. "You're our number one producer in the United States," he said. "The Cali bosses are grateful for your work."

While Isabella appreciated the accolades, she was nervous about why David was calling her and not Diego. "I tried to contact Diego before calling you back, but I couldn't get hold of him," she said.

"That's because he's with me. I want you to fly to Cali for a meeting with the bosses," he said. "Diego is already here for the meeting."

Isabella thought this was strange. She was sure Diego would have said something if he was leaving. "Okay," she replied cautiously, "When do you want me there?"

"As soon as possible. When you get your flight scheduled, call me back and let me know the date and times."

Isabella was scared to death. She had no idea what was going on. *Did the Cali cartel think she was stealing, or was this business as usual to have a meeting like this? Diego never told her about such meetings. Why didn't Diego tell her he was flying back to Colombia?* She was terrified and felt sick about it. She drove home and told Juanita.

Now Juanita was scared for Isabella. "What do you think of this?" she asked.

"I don't know," Isabella replied, "David congratulated me for my excellent work, so I don't think I'm in trouble. But I'm still nervous."

Isabella took some money from her closet and went to a travel agent that she knew Colombians used for travel. The agent made flight reservations for the next day but questioned her about the urgent departure because it cost twice the normal ticket. "Thank you, but I've got a sick relative that I have to see right away," she replied.

Isabella drove to the first pay phone she saw and paged David. He called back within 30 minutes. "I'm leaving tomorrow morning and will arrive in Cali tomorrow night at 9:35," she told him.

"I'll have my driver pick you up."

"How will I recognize him?"

"He'll be waiting for you with a sign with your name on it. You won't miss him—He's easy to see."

*****

The next morning, Juanita drove Isabella to Los Angeles International Airport. They barely spoke. When they arrived at Tom Bradley International Terminal, Juanita started crying.

"I'm so worried for you!"

Isabella, as always, stayed strong. "Everything will be all right," she said as they embraced, "Please don't worry—I promise I'll be back soon."

Two hours later, Isabella was in the air for the nearly ten-hour flight to Cali, Colombia. She was tired, as she had barely slept the night before. She took a sleeping pill and was fast asleep, but she had nightmares.

The next thing Isabella felt was the landing gear touching the ground as the wheels grabbed the asphalt. She was startled awake and the realization set in. She knew she was in too deep to get out of the business now. If she tried, the cartel would probably kill her family in Colombia. It was all or nothing now. She had to dedicate her life to the business and do whatever it took to survive.

The closer she got to her destination, the harder her heart pounded. She had heard horror stories about how ruthless the bosses of drug cartels could be. The only thing preventing her from having a panic attack was knowing that she had done nothing wrong. She had only made the bosses very rich.

Isabella exited the plane and walked with everyone else to customs. All she had with her was a carry-on. She thought she'd have to wait in a long line to get through, as it is always the worst part of any trip, but not this time. As she was getting in line, an airport employee approached her and escorted her to the front of the line.

As Isabella walked to the front of the line, she saw the driver who was there to pick her up. How could she not notice him! He was a very large man, six foot four, wearing a short-sleeved shirt that showed off his muscles. He was just on the other side of the customs agents, holding up a piece of paper with her name on it. *Obviously, someone was paid off to get me through customs quickly,* she thought. She was cleared through customs right away. They asked for her passport, looked at it briefly, and moved her forward.

Isabella walked up to the enormous man holding the paper and said, "I'm Isabella."

The man smiled. "They told me you were pretty—they weren't kidding."

Isabella ignored the comment and asked him his name. "Jorge," he replied. He reached for Isabella's carry-on, but she pushed his hand away and said, "I got it."

He shrugged and said, "Follow me."

They exited the airport where a large black Suburban with tinted windows was waiting. Isabella could see another large man behind the wheel. Jorge said, "This is our ride." And then he opened the back passenger door. She got in and set her carry-on next to her on the seat. The driver never said a word or even looked at her. Jorge got into the front passenger seat and off they went.

"Don't get too comfortable, we won't be in the car long," Jorge cautioned. Isabella could see they were headed for a smaller section of the airport, where there were private planes and helicopters. They parked at a large hangar. Jorge opened the door for Isabella. "We'll be flying the rest of the way," he said. Isabella was getting a little nervous but felt she had no choice but to go along with Jorge. They walked around to the far side of the large hangar, and a helicopter started its engine. Jorge pointed to the helicopter, "Hop in." She nodded and climbed in the rear seat, while the pilot handed her some ear protectors. Jorge got in the front passenger seat, put his ear protectors on, and gave the pilot a thumbs-up.

The helicopter lifted off and sped into the darkness. Isabella could see they were flying away from the bright lights of Cali and into the jungle of Colombia. About an hour later, Isabella could see a place in the distance that was well-lit. It appeared to be a ranch.

As they landed, several men ran over and greeted the pilot and Jorge. The men were dressed like ranch hands—cowboy boots, hats, and jeans. One of the men handed Jorge a walkie-talkie, and then they left. Jorge helped Isabella from the helicopter and grabbed her carry-on. When she reached toward him to get it back, Jorge pulled it away and said, "We need to search this."

They walked over to a Jeep, and Jorge helped Isabella into the front passenger seat. Before he got in, he spoke to someone on the walkie-talkie, but Isabella couldn't make out what he was saying. When he finished his conversation, he climbed into the driver's seat and looked at Isabella. He could tell she was nervous. "Don't worry," he said, "You're among friends."

Isabella nodded, "Where are we?"

"We're on the bosses' ranch."

"You mean David, right?"

Jorge laughed. "No. David's here for business, just like you. This ranch belongs to Gilberto Rodriguez."

Isabella was taken aback as Gilberto and Miguel Rodriguez were the head of the Cali cartel. *Now I am officially scared!* she thought.

As they drove down a hill, Isabella could see a mansion up on an adjacent hill. The mansion was beautiful and all lit up. "I'm taking you to a guesthouse where you'll stay tonight," Jorge explained.

"When is the meeting that I've been called here for?"

"I believe it's scheduled for tomorrow or the following day," he replied. "But for tonight, you need to get some sleep. You've got a big day tomorrow."

Jorge drove up to a large house—not quite a mansion, but it was a big house with a pool. "This is the guesthouse where you'll be staying." Isabella was wide-eyed. She couldn't believe how big and lavish it was.

A young woman in her twenties greeted them as they got out of the Jeep. Jorge introduced her to Isabella as Anna. "Anna will be here to assist you during your stay. If you are hungry or need anything, you are to ask her," he said. Isabella was stunned. She couldn't believe she was staying in this huge house and had her own servant. Jorge told Anna to take Isabella into the house and show her to her room. "I'll bring your carry-on to you in a moment," he said. She knew Jorge was going to search it, but she wasn't worried—she only brought clothes and makeup.

Anna gave Isabella a tour of the house and the surrounding property, which were exquisite. "Are you hungry?" Anna asked. "Can I get you anything to eat or drink?"

"Yes, thank you. Some water and something to eat. I'm hungry after all that traveling."

Anna brought Isabella water and asked, "Would you like a turkey sandwich?"

"Yes, that would be great."

Anna used the housephone and called for a turkey sandwich. A short time later, a well-dressed room service attendant arrived with a turkey sandwich and a beautiful fruit platter. She ate in the dining room at a huge table.

She was nearly done eating when a tall thin older man with salt-and-pepper hair arrived. Anna got up from the table and left the room, so Isabella was alone with the man. The man reached out and shook her hand and introduced himself as David.

When Isabella heard his name, she quickly stood up and said, "So nice to finally meet you."

"Likewise."

"Is everything all right?" she asked. "Where is Diego?"

David assured Isabella that everything was fine and that everyone was called here for a meeting. "Mr. Rodriguez has recognized your hard work and he wanted to meet you in person. You'll meet him tomorrow. But the business meeting you've been called here for will take place elsewhere, without Mr. Rodríguez," he explained.

Isabella acknowledged him.

"You must be tired. I'm leaving so you can get some rest," he said.

A short time later, Anna returned with Isabella's carry-on and said, "I'm going to get some sleep. You should probably do the same. If you need anything, just pick up the housephone and dial 1. That will connect you with me."

Isabella realized she was exhausted. Finally, with a moment to herself, she decided to take a much-needed shower after a long day of traveling. She was in awe. The bathroom was bigger than her bedroom back in California. She then crawled into bed and quickly went to sleep. Tomorrow was indeed going to be a big day, bigger than she could have imagined.

CHAPTER
20

Dawn was breaking at the sprawling ranch. Soft footsteps approached the front door of one of the guesthouses. A masked hit man attached a silencer to his handgun. He knocked on the door. Inside the bedroom of the guesthouse, the knocking woke up Andres.

Still groggy, Diego's partner in Southern California put on a robe. As he walked to the door, his irritation grew. *What the hell is going on at this hour?* he wondered. On the other side of the door, the hit man gripped the gun at his side.

*****

Diego raced out of a horse's stable. He ran through an open field toward the outskirts of the ranch, within sight of a hillside forest. He looked over his shoulder in panic. Gunshots rang out. A bullet ripped through Diego's right thigh. He clutched his leg and fell to the ground. He crawled forward. He wasn't far from the shelter of the forest. A hit man caught up to him, brandishing an Uzi. Diego's eyes grew wide.

"I can pay you back."

"Too late. We don't trust you."

The hit man aimed the Uzi at Diego's prone body. A hail of bullets obliterated him in an instant.

*****

Two corpses floated down the slow current of the Rio Cauca. The flowing waters washed away the blood but not the bullet holes.

CHAPTER
21

L ater that morning, Anna entered the guesthouse and told Isabella breakfast would be served at eight o'clock with Mr. Gilberto Rodriguez in the main house. Isabella felt a chill. She was nervous about meeting the head of the Cali cartel. She got up and got ready for the day.

Anna returned to pick up Isabella for breakfast. They went outside where Jorge was waiting in the Jeep. "Did you sleep well?" Jorge asked.

Isabella was growing more anxious by the minute. "Yes," she replied, "I slept very well, thank you."

As Jorge drove to the main house, Isabella saw how stunning the ranch was. They drove by a large stable where horses were being fed and attended to. As they reached the main house, she saw that it was situated high on a plateau overlooking a large valley. Jorge told Isabella that the boss, Gilberto Rodriguez, owned all the land as far as one could see.

They approached the main house and several servants came out to escort Isabella and Anna inside. Anna informed Isabella that she would see her after breakfast.

"Why aren't you coming?" Isabella asked.

"I wasn't invited."

Isabella was escorted to a beautiful room with a breakfast table fully decorated. The view was breathtaking. Isabella stared out the immense window at the mountain ranges. She heard a smooth baritone voice nearby. "Isn't it wonderful?" Gilberto Rodriguez approached and extended his hand. He introduced himself and asked her to make herself comfortable and take a seat. Isabella noted that Gilberto was not a very big man and spoke in a soft, friendly manner. "I am very impressed with your work in the United States," he remarked.

"Thank you, Mr. Rodriguez," Isabella said. Isabella wasn't as nervous as she expected to be in Gilberto's presence.

Platters of food were brought to the table. Isabella asked, "Will David and Diego be joining us for breakfast?"

"No, just us," he said with a smile. "I want to get to know the person who is making me so much money in the United States. David will join us after breakfast."

Isabella was surprised that during their breakfast together, Gilberto never talked about his drug empire—he spoke only about his ranch and her. After breakfast, he stood and shook her hand again and said, "It was nice meeting you. I wish you good luck with your business in California." David walked in the room while Isabella was thanking Gilberto. As he left, Gilberto commented, "You're right, David, Isabella is a lovely person. I'll leave you two alone."

"Did you enjoy your breakfast?" David asked.

"Oh yes," Isabella replied, "Mr. Rodriguez is very nice."

David smiled. "Follow me."

They walked back outside where Jorge waited in the Jeep. David got in the front and Isabella in the back. She noticed that her carry-on was on the seat next to her.

"Am I going back home to California?" she asked.

"Yes, but first we're meeting with some other people. It's about an hour away. So please, put on your seat belt and enjoy the ride."

*****

Before long, they arrived at another large ranch. Isabella had no idea where they were. She only knew they were in the hills just outside Cali. Jorge opened Isabella's door and David asked her to accompany him into the house. Isabella realized she was far more nervous with David than with Mr. Rodriguez. David was rigid and all business.

David escorted Isabella into a large room. Seated at a table in the middle of the room were two other men. "Please sit," David directed, motioning to a chair at the table. The two other men at the table didn't get up, nor did they introduce themselves. David said, "No names will be exchanged here. These two men will contact you by pager and reference this meeting as to who they are."

Isabella nodded and said, "Will Diego be joining us today?"

David's demeanor got even more rigid, if that was possible. He looked directly at Isabella, "Diego is no longer working for this organization." Isabella sensed this information wasn't good for Diego and didn't respond.

"Many changes are happening in our business and many more are still in the works. Diego was one of them. Due to your business production and the knowledge you've demonstrated, you will take over the Cali operations in Southern California."

Isabella was shocked, and David could read it on her face. "Don't worry," he assured her. "You'll have plenty of help."

David motioned to the two men at the table. "These two gentlemen will supply you with the people and money you'll need to expand your operation."

For the next hour, they discussed the new drug-smuggling routes into the United States. Isabella spoke up and told them how the new routes through the west coast have already increased her business. David immediately interjected, "Business will only get busier now. You need to be able to trust the people working for you." He reminded Isabella as he pointed his index finger at her from across the table, "This is important because you'll be responsible for any lost product. It's all good, though, because you'll be compensated very well."

A wave of conflicting emotions washed over Isabella, though she tried not to show any outward signs. First, what a relief that she was mistaken! She wasn't in trouble, and her life wasn't in danger. However, her immersion in the drug world was now total. There was a somber acceptance. She was aware that if she turned down this offer, she would disappear like Diego. So, Isabella told David she was eager to get home and get started. David grinned, "You're leaving for the United States on a late flight out of Cali tonight."

Jorge returned with Isabella's carry-on and gave it to her. "The helicopter will be here in an hour to take you to the airport," David said. "Make yourself comfortable—there's a bedroom with a shower if you'd like to freshen up before you leave." Isabella thanked him, grabbed her carry-on, and carried it into the back bedroom. She didn't feel comfortable taking a shower with these men in the house, so she splashed some water on her face and changed her clothes.

An hour later, Isabella heard the helicopter flying in. She waited with her carry-on next to the front entrance. David approached and shook her hand and said, "I'll talk to you soon. Jorge will escort you to the airport. Good luck."

Isabella boarded the helicopter and flew back to the Cali airport, touching down at the same large hangar as before. She was driven to the airport terminal by the same driver and Jorge, but this time, Jorge didn't escort her into the airport. He helped Isabella with her door and carry-on, and then said goodbye.

Isabella went through customs and waited for her flight. She boarded and was thankful no one else was seated in her row—she had a lot on her mind and didn't feel like making small talk. She only wanted to think about what was ahead for her.

*****

Isabella's flight landed at LAX and once again, she stood in line to get through customs. It was early and Isabella didn't want to call Juanita for a ride, so she took a cab to her townhouse.

It was almost noon by the time she walked through her front door. She called for Juanita, but there was no answer. Isabella checked her bedroom and noticed the bed was made, but she wasn't home. Isabella was feeling tired but had some energy to burn off and was hungry. Before she left for Cali, she had given Juanita a pager through Gustavo.

Isabella wanted to see Juanita, so she drove to a pay phone and paged her. She received a call back immediately. Juanita was so excited to hear from her.

"Are you hungry?" Isabella asked. "I'm starving! Let's get some lunch and I'll tell you all about my trip."

"Meet me at the Scorpion in thirty minutes," Juanita said.

Isabella and Juanita pulled into the parking lot at the same time and both were smiling ear to ear. As they embraced, Juanita said, "I was so scared you wouldn't come back!"

Isabella led the way into the restaurant. "I'll tell you everything over lunch."

During their hour-and-a-half lunch, Isabella divulged it all. She told Juanita about Diego and his disappearance. She described how scared she was when meeting with David, but not with Mr. Rodriguez. She also told her how nice Mr. Rodriguez was, and how he never talked about his business—just about her and his ranch. Isabella said, "It was strange. You'd never know he was the boss of the Cali cartel."

She continued, "Now that I'm going to be responsible for a big portion of the cocaine coming into California, I'll need to recruit a few friends from back home that I can trust."

"When will all of this start?" Juanita was nervous and excited for Isabella.

"I don't know exactly but probably within a couple of months."

Over the next three years, Isabella built a large drug distribution organization in California. She had her hands on about 80 percent of the cocaine coming into California.

CHAPTER
22

Right around the same time that Isabella began building her drug empire, the Torrance Police Department's narcotic task force gained a crucial break when in January 1986, one of Detective Mattson's drug cartel suspects turned informant. Detective Mattson, with a judge's approval, had the informant released from custody under tight restrictions.

Basically, the informant couldn't move or even breathe without getting approval from his handler—in this case, Detective Mattson. If the informant did something without Detective Mattson's knowledge, the informant would be rearrested, and the other members of the drug cartel would find out he was working with the police. This was obviously detrimental to the well-being of the informant.

In this particular case, Detective Mattson's informant was instructed by a higher-ranking cartel member to meet with a person named Poncho and set up a 150-kilo cocaine pickup. The street value for 150 kilos of pure cocaine was about $15 million. The key to the success of this operation for Detective Mattson and our team was to surveil our informant in his first meeting with Poncho.

In the Colombian drug cartel business, one expected the unexpected. Anything good or bad could happen at any time. Sometimes at a first meeting like this one, the meeting was just that, a meet and greet only—no drugs or money exchanged. Other times, a large drug or money exchange might occur.

The best-case scenario and objective was to surveil the meeting between the informant and the other drug cartel member. After the meeting was over, our team would then surveil this new drug cartel member and bed—find out where he slept at night—him down. Our team would then set up surveillance on the drug cartel member's residence and follow him day and night to see where he went and with whom he met.

Most drug cartel members at the level of our informant only organized transfers of cocaine and money—they generally weren't the ones actually transferring cocaine and money. The drug cartel members who had hands on and moved the cocaine or money were referred to as mules. So, at the end of the case, it was important for the narcotic team to tie in all the places the drug cartel members visited.

Locating all residences the drug cartel members used for their drug enterprise was essential for the successful conclusion of a case. After a narcotic case was concluded and people were arrested, all the places we surveilled the drug cartel members to, would be searched for kilos of cocaine, marijuana, money, and evidence to connect them to the drug cartel business.

By this time in our training, all aspects of our undercover operations ran like clockwork. Team members dressed as normal, clean-cut civilians to blend in with the crowd. In contrast, the members of the crime impact team gave the appearance of bad asses because that was the type of people they aimed to take down.

The narcotic team drove common Toyota and Honda sedans in varying colors and sizes. On the passenger seat, detectives kept a small gym bag, which we called a war bag. In this bag we stored a Colt .380 Mustang handgun, extra ammo for the .380, a Colt .45 (which was placed on the driver's seat under a leg), a police portable radio, and a leg holster. All detectives also carried small pagers. The .380 handgun, in contrast to the powerful Colt .45, was small and easy to conceal in a pocket, waistband, or ankle holster. It was the weapon of choice when a surveillance suddenly turned into a foot pursuit.

The informant's meet and greet with Poncho went as planned. Our narcotic team surveilled our informant to the city of Panorama. When our informant pulled into a Shell gas station and filled up his black Honda Accord with gas, we watched as he walked up to a pay phone in the parking lot.

Detective Mack had the eye, meaning he was watching our informant from his undercover car and relaying his actions to us via his radio. The rest of us stayed near and set up our directions of travel to be ready when our informant went mobile again.

Detective Mack broadcast, "Our informant made a call on the pay phone and hung up." Twenty minutes passed before he advised us, "Our informant picked up the pay phone and is talking. The conversation was quick—he hung up. Now he is getting back into his Honda. He just drove out of the gas station and onto the street."

Detective Carroll followed our informant and started calling the surveillance. The informant drove only about half a mile down the road and pulled into a McDonald's. Detective Sears pulled into the McDonald's lot at the same time. Detective Sears parked and entered McDonald's before our informant even got out of his car.

Sergeant Tilly advised he was parked across the street and had the eye on our informant and his black Honda Accord. The rest of the team set up in their undercover cars, covering all directions of travel. Sergeant Tilly broadcast, "The informant has exited his car and is walking into McDonald's." He told everyone to lay low, as the drug cartel member our informant was to meet, might be surveilling the area, looking for a tail.

Five minutes after our informant entered McDonald's, Detective Sears, using his handheld portable radio said, "Our informant just sat down at a table with a middle-aged Latino—balding, wearing a red shirt and jeans."

Sergeant Tilly acknowledged Detective Sears and added, "Make sure all exits to McDonald's are covered." Detective Mack and I confirmed that we had the three exits covered, along with the rear employee exit. Sergeant Tilly, while still on the eye, watching our informant's car, said, "Everyone be ready, we'll surveil this new player in the red shirt that our informant is meeting." We all acknowledged that we understood.

Forty minutes later, our informant walked out of McDonald's with the new player in the red shirt. Sergeant Tilly advised, "Our informant and this new player just shook hands and are walking to their cars. The new player is getting into a dark-green Toyota Celica. He's backing out of the parking stall and is now exiting onto the street. He's headed westbound toward the I-405."

Detective Sears came on the air, "Did everyone see the new player?" Sergeant Tilly was still calling the surveillance, so he let Detective Sears know we did and were following him. Sergeant Tilly was two cars back of the new player in his dark-green Celica. He advised that the Celica was setting up to enter the I-405 northbound.

Sergeant Tilly then broadcast, "The Celica is northbound on the on-ramp of the I-405. I no longer have the eye on the Celica." Sergeant Tilly kept driving straight to avoid detection.

As the Celica merged onto the I-405, Detective Mattson said, "I'm two cars back of the Toyota Celica." He continued to call the surveillance of the new player in the Celica. Mattson broadcast, "The Celica is driving at a high rate of speed. He's crossed all lanes and settled into the fast lane and is driving about 80 miles per hour."

Detective Carroll announced, "I'm out front of the Celica and in the same lane with three cars between us." Detective Mattson told him to take over the surveillance since he was out in front. The traffic was light, so all lanes of traffic were traveling above the speed limit. Detective Mattson changed lanes to the number three lane, anticipating our new player would get off the freeway soon. Detective Carroll advised, "The Celica is changing lanes and appears to be getting onto the 118 Freeway east."

Detective Mack said, "I have the call. The Toyota Celica just merged onto the 118 Freeway east. The Celica has slowed down and is only traveling about 60 miles per hour. It's now in the number two lane in moderate traffic." The rest of the team were in lanes three and four, anticipating the Celica getting off the freeway.

Suddenly, the Celica crossed all lanes of the freeway and exited on Glenoaks Boulevard. I was now on the eye, calling the surveillance. I was right behind the Celica as I called the surveillance with my radio mic between my legs and both hands on the steering wheel, just in case the new player saw me in his rearview mirror. Detective Sears was behind me and took over the call, as we were at the bottom of the off-ramp and stopped at a red light.

When the light turned green, we made a right turn, following the Celica. As we approached the first cross street, I made a right turn out of the Celica's view, in case he was watching me. Detective Sears continued to call the surveillance of the Celica when it abruptly made a left turn down a neighborhood street. The lighting was poor, and we weren't able to see the street name he had turned on.

Detective Mack made a right turn on the same street, driving in the opposite direction while calling the surveillance through his rearview mirror. He pulled to the curb and continued to call the surveillance. Sergeant Tilly turned left in the direction of the Celica. Everyone else paralleled the streets north and south of the Celica. Sergeant Tilly called, "The Celica just pulled into the driveway of a small white house with blue trim, located about mid-block. I no longer have a view of our new player." The team immediately covered both ends of the street in case the new player went mobile again.

Fifteen minutes went by. Detective Carroll drove down the street and located the house with the Celica parked in the driveway. He drove about seventy-five yards past the house and pulled over where he could keep surveillance of the area in case the Celica or another car from the house went mobile again. Detective Mattson broadcast, "I'm at a pay phone and will call my informant to get intel about our new player." Sergeant Tilly looked at his Thomas Guide map book and let everyone know we were in the city of Pacoima, a small city in the San Fernando Valley in Los Angeles County.

Twenty-five minutes passed before Detective Mattson completed his phone call with his informant. He advised the team, "My informant tells me this new player is his connection who's setting up the deal for 150 kilos of cocaine. He's known as Poncho. Poncho said the load of cocaine is on its way from Mexico and should be here within a month or so."

Our informant asked Poncho if this load was big enough for the 150 kilos of cocaine he was instructed to pick up. Poncho told our informant the load of cocaine was coming from a high-ranking member of the Cali Drug Cartel, from whom he had received loads in the past. He also told our informant the high-ranking Cali Drug Cartel member was a very attractive Colombian female, and his boss was the only one who dealt with her—he himself had never spoken to her. He told our informant that when the cocaine was in place, he would get ahold of him to pick up his share.

As always, our team discussed our game plan. But this time, it was especially exciting. We had a possible Cali Drug Cartel kingpin in our sights. The hierarchy chart of the cartel's operations in Southern California, posted on our briefing room wall, was finally taking shape. At the lowest level of the chart, we had our informant. Above him was Poncho. One more level up was Poncho's boss. At the top was the high-ranking female. We didn't have a photo of her yet, but a female silhouette now occupied the crown of the chart.

We had our ultimate target on the wall. The question became, could the team hit a bull's-eye?

CHAPTER
23

Poncho was not only a prime suspect but was also our best chance at getting closer to the cartel queen. He became the focal point of our surveillances in hopes of locating his stash house and higher-level cartel connections.

Every day at 6:00 a.m., Sergeant Tilly and our narcotic team would set up outside Poncho's house in Pacoima. It was critical in all cases to set up on our primary subject early, so we could establish a pattern for him—like when he got up or left his house for the day. It was no different for Poncho.

For over a month, we continued our surveillance. This was tough on us all—Pacoima, on a good day with no traffic, was an hour's drive from the area of Torrance, where most of us lived.

For that entire month, nothing Poncho did indicated that a load of cocaine had come in, but we did identify several potential properties he might have been using as stash houses. We concluded this by observing Poncho's driving habits to these properties, one was an apartment in Culver City and the other was a house in Santa Clarita—both were in Los Angeles County.

Poncho visited both properties three times in that month. Each time, he used anti-surveillance techniques to see if anyone was following him. He drove aggressively fast, ran red lights, then pulled to the curb and looked at the driver of every car that passed him.

Our surveillance team immediately caught on to this anti-surveillance maneuver. In order to counter this attempt, the team member calling the mobile surveillance was deployed out in front of Poncho, not behind. Like most drug cartel members, Poncho always looked behind him to see if he was being followed. Being in front allowed other narcotic team members to lie way back or to parallel from other streets during the surveillance.

As with all our cases, we followed up on every location Poncho visited. We investigated who lived at the apartment in Culver City and the house in Santa Clarita. We learned that both properties were owned by separate people, but the utilities for each property were in the same name. Poncho used his own key to let himself into each property, which just added to our suspicion that they were potential future stash houses for money or kilos of cocaine for this drug cartel organization.

In our experience, drug cartel members rarely kept money and cocaine in the same location. Ninety-nine percent of the time, they used two locations—one for drugs and one for money from the sale of the drugs. The drug cartels hoped that if the police busted them, they would only find one stash house. Another reason both locations looked suspicious is that we didn't see anyone come in or out of either place.

With only six members, including the sergeant, it would be nearly impossible for our team to conduct a surveillance of two potential drug cartel locations—it would have required splitting the team in half. So, Sergeant Tilly called on Sergeant Dalton's crime impact team to help surveil the apartment in Culver City and the house in Santa Clarita. Our objective was to see if anyone was actually living in either location.

Although Sergeant Dalton's crime impact team didn't really enjoy surveilling vacant homes, they did so out of professionalism. Their team knew that sooner or later, they'd need our narcotic team to help them too. But sitting on vacant homes for days, made the hours go by very slowly.

After three days, Sergeant Dalton's crime impact team saw no one come in or out of either location. Sergeant Tilly felt confident no one was living in either place, and he believed it was highly likely that one or both places were stash houses. Sergeant Tilly let Sergeant Dalton's crime impact team go back to their regular cases until things got more heated. Sergeant Dalton, to the dismay of his crime impact team, told Sergeant Tilly they'd be ready when needed.

Surveilling a drug cartel organization is very different from surveilling a career criminal committing violent crimes. One needs more patience on a drug cartel case, which is why the personalities of a narcotic cop and a crime-fighter cop were, for the most part, very different. It also made things interesting when they helped each other out on cases. Both Sergeants Tilly and Dalton truly had to use their best leadership skills in order to keep their team's patient and respectful toward each other.

When the crime impact team returned to their cases, Sergeant Tilly and his narcotic team continued to surveil Poncho. Once you knew someone's daily routine, surveillance was pretty easy. It was when drug cartel members changed their daily routines and started to use anti-surveillance techniques to hide a cocaine or money delivery, that things got really interesting.

Poncho wasn't doing much. It looked as if he was entertaining out-of-town relatives. One day we followed him to Los Angeles International Airport where he picked up two adults and a small child. For a week, we followed Poncho and the family as they went to Universal Studios, Disneyland, and other tourist locations. This was when surveillances got really boring, and it was hard to stay focused. But it was important that we continue to follow Poncho—you never knew when he'd get a call that a load of cocaine had arrived.

One morning after two months of constant surveillance, Poncho left his house in Pacoima at 10:00 a.m. Our surveillance team followed him as he drove to a nearby pay phone and made a couple of phone calls. It was imperative to document all our observations of the movements of the drug cartel members during a surveillance. Our narcotic team had a case agent who oversaw the investigation and was responsible for documenting all movements of whoever we were following. This was known as the daily log.

The case agent's task was to keep a daily log of the team's and the drug cartel's activity. They documented detailed descriptions of people the drug cartel members met, the locations they went to, the cars they drove, and the pay phone numbers they used. These details helped tie the drug cartel members to one another and show they all worked for the same illegal enterprise.

As a case agent, you wrote warrants daily to obtain information about the actual owners of residences where drug cartel members lived or visited. The case agent ran the registration of every car or truck driven by a drug cartel member and of the persons he met to find the name and address that the car was registered to. In most cases, the car or truck was registered to a PO box, which indicated that a suspect was attempting to hide his or her identity. In some cases, we discovered several vehicles from our current case and prior cases using the same PO box as an address.

During a surveillance, we would take as many pictures as possible of every drug cartel member and the people they met. We also obtained pictures from the Department of Motor Vehicles (DMV) of the registered owners of the cars we followed. In almost all cases, the person we photographed driving a car didn't match the photo of the registered owner from the DMV. This was a common tactic the drug cartels used to hide their illegal activity and their members' identity from law enforcement.

At the end of each day, the case agent used his daily logs to update his ongoing search warrant. Updating the search warrant was imperative since it saved the agent from having to document the long list of activities and facts that had occurred on prior dates. As cases progressed, narcotic search warrants and attachments could quickly become hundreds of pages.

So, on that morning, we watched Poncho make calls from a pay phone. We knew his first call wasn't a pager because he started talking immediately. The conversation lasted three minutes as documented by case agent Detective Mattson. We could tell Poncho's second call was to a pager because he dialed a number and then hung up. He then returned to his car, leaned against it, crossed his arms, faced the traffic, and looked into each car that passed. It was clear he was waiting for a return call from someone he had just paged. Fifteen minutes later, the pay phone rang. Poncho answered, talked for five minutes, then he returned to his car and left.

As Poncho drove away, I went to the pay phone he had just used, got the phone number and address of the phone, and noted the time that Poncho used it so I could give it to Detective Mattson for his daily log. We could then link drug cartel members by identifying pager numbers and the pay phones they used. We then created a link analysis chart that connected pagers of arrestees and the pay phones they used. This could be used in court to link the drug cartel members to each other.

Once I obtained the pay phone information, I played catch-up with the team that was following Poncho. While I was catching up, Detective Mattson broadcast, "I just received a page from our informant with a 911 after the phone number."

The team followed Poncho back to his Pacoima home. As soon as Poncho parked his car and entered his house, Detective Mattson drove to a pay phone and called his informant.

"What's going on?" Detective Mattson asked.

"Poncho said the load of cocaine is in. I should have my 150 kilos within a few days."

As Detective Mattson was talking to his informant, the surveillance team observed Poncho exit his house and get into his car. Detective Carroll, who was on the eye, said, "Poncho changed from sweats and a T-shirt to nice slacks and a collared shirt." Detective Mattson heard that the team was mobile again, following Poncho. He quickly ended the call with his informant and drove like a madman to catch up.

Detective Sears was out front calling the surveillance while other team members were either way back or paralleling the surveillance. He said, "We're on approach to the 118 Freeway. I won't get on the freeway, but I'll let you know if Poncho does."

Detective Mack immediately positioned himself in the number three lane, closest to the curb, three cars from Poncho, who was in the number one lane on Glenoaks Boulevard approaching the 118 Freeway westbound on-ramp. Detective Mack took over the surveillance call. He exclaimed, "Poncho whamboed across all lanes and onto the 118 Freeway westbound. He just cut off several cars!"

Detective Mack was in the perfect position to follow Poncho onto the freeway without being detected. All the other members of the team were able to do the same, except Detective Sears, who made a quick U-turn and drove back to catch up. Detective Mack broadcast, "Looks like it's game time, boys." We knew this meant that Poncho's driving habits had changed, and a load of cocaine was in.

The freeway traffic was moderate, and Detective Mack continued calling the surveillance from the number two lane while Poncho was in the fast lane. The other members stayed in the slower lanes in case Poncho made another sudden move across all lanes. We positioned ourselves this way, so we could quickly get off the freeway with Poncho without him seeing cars driving erratically behind him. The exception would be Detective Mack, who would go straight and play catch-up.

Detective Mack was still on the call as they approached the I-405. Anticipating that Poncho might get on to the I-405, he easily moved over into the number three lane as traffic in the number three and four lanes was going the same speed as Poncho's lane. Suddenly, as Poncho approached the I-405, he sped up, crossed all lanes, and entered the I-405 south, toward Santa Monica. Detective Mack and the other surveillance team members were in a great position and entered the I-405 south without having to make any crazy lane changes.

Detective Mack continued to call the surveillance as Poncho traveled south in the number two lane on the I-405. Traffic was much busier on the I-405, so Mack called the surveillance from the same lane, but three cars back. All the other surveillance units stayed in the slower lanes. They had gone six miles when Detective Mack announced Poncho moved to the number three lane just as the US 101 was approaching. The other surveillance team members all moved over into the number four lane, anticipating Poncho suddenly getting on the US 101.

115

Detective Mack called, "Poncho just cut off some cars—he switched over into the number four lane and merged onto the US 101 north."

I took over the call and broadcast, "Poncho merged over into the number two lane, US 101 north." It was 5:00 p.m., so traffic was very heavy. I positioned myself in the number one lane, the fast lane. It was a toss-up as to which lane was moving faster.

I called out to Detective Mack, asking if he had heard where we were, as he was still playing catch-up. Mack said he had just exited the I-405 and was taking surface streets to catch up. My lane was now moving faster than Poncho's number two lane and I passed him. I gradually switched to Poncho's lane and called the surveillance from two cars in front. I broadcast, "I just passed Poncho and he is fixed to his rearview mirror—looking for a tail."

I continued to call the surveillance as we approached the Tampa Avenue off-ramp. I called out, "Poncho has his blinker on to change lanes into the number three lane, but no one is letting him over." This gave the surveillance team time to switch into the slow lane. Poncho finally changed lanes to the number three, then to the number four lane, and exited the US 101 at Tampa Avenue.

Sergeant Tilly took over the call. I was off the surveillance, as I couldn't get off at Tampa Avenue without Poncho noticing me. Detective Mack was back up with the surveillance and made better time on the surface streets. Sergeant Tilly broadcast, "Poncho made a left turn on Tampa Avenue at the bottom of the off-ramp." Everyone else followed except me, as I was now playing catch-up.

Sergeant Tilly called out, "Poncho is in the number two lane on Tampa Avenue. I'm in the number one lane and I'm passing him." Sergeant Tilly continued to call the surveillance out in front of Poncho with three cars between them. Sergeant Tilly confirmed, "Poncho is looking in his rearview and side mirrors." As Poncho and the surveillance team came up on a red traffic light, he gutter-sniped everyone — meaning he drove on the far-right side of the roadway, which wasn't a lane, but he had enough room to get through.

Poncho approached the red light, looked both ways, and ran it. Sergeant Tilly still had sights on him, but Poncho was pulling away, out of sight, as the surveillance team couldn't run a red light without being detected. Good thing was, I had been paralleling the surveillance since I exited the freeway. I was out in front of Poncho; waiting for him. Once Poncho was out of sight from Sergeant Tilly and the rest of the surveillance team, they all ran the red light to catch up to him.

I called out, "I have Poncho in my sight and I'm out in front of him, still southbound Tampa Avenue, entering the city of Tarzana."

Suddenly, Poncho pulled into a parking lot and out of my view. By then, Detective Carroll had the call and saw Poncho park in a strip mall parking lot at Plummer Street and Tampa Avenue. The other members of the surveillance team quickly set up to cover all directions of travel in case Poncho started to drive again. Detective Carroll noted several open businesses in the strip mall, one being a Jack's Burgers. Carroll broadcast, "Poncho is just sitting in his car."

Sergeant Tilly called, "I think Poncho is there to meet someone important—"

Detective Carroll interrupted and said, "Poncho just exited his car and is walking into Jack's Burgers."

Detective Mack knew the area well and advised, "This is a multicultural neighborhood. We can send someone in to see if Poncho is meeting with someone—it won't be a problem."

Sergeant Tilly asked Mack, "Are you in a position to enter the restaurant?"

"Yes, I am. I'll be off the air."

Detective Mack entered Jack's Burgers and ordered food. As he did, he noticed Poncho was sitting by himself to the rear of the restaurant, near the exit doors. Detective Mack ordered his food, then went to the restroom. When he returned from the restroom, he saw a thin Latino wearing a brown leather jacket now sitting with Poncho. He noticed that Poncho had his food, but the Latino in the leather jacket did not. Mack sat down and ate, all the while keeping an eye on Poncho and the new player.

The new player hadn't ordered food and he was doing most of the talking. It appeared this was a business meeting and not just two friends having dinner. The new player suddenly got up and left through the exit doors. Detective Mack nonchalantly grabbed his drink and walked out the entrance of the restaurant to his car and broadcast, "Poncho had a meeting with a Latino wearing a brown leather jacket, who left through the back exit doors."

Detective Mattson came on air and said, "I'm following the new player in the leather jacket. He's driving a beige Nissan Sentra northbound on Tampa Avenue." He told everyone to catch up because he wanted to bed this guy down. We all heard Detective Mattson's request, but we were three blocks away and rushing to help when the new player drove down a one-way street and Mattson couldn't go with him.

Our team was in the area and we began looking for the beige Nissan Sentra. After five minutes and no sight of the new player or his Nissan Sentra, the team returned to Jack's Burgers to see if Poncho was still there. But no luck, Poncho was gone now too. Sergeant Tilly broadcast, "Everyone, head back to Poncho's house and we'll see if he returns."

Back at Poncho's house, we found his car in the driveway. We all agreed we needed to stay on Poncho from sunup until he went to bed. It was 9:00 p.m., and the lights were still on, so we set up surveillance. Detective Mattson left to do follow-up investigative work and update his warrant. Poncho finally turned out the lights at 11:00 p.m. and our surveillance for the night ended. We finally all went home.

Needless to say, it takes a lot of persistence and patience to be a good detective. While a new player might have slipped by us, we weren't giving up on Poncho.

CHAPTER
24

After several long days and nights surveilling Poncho and Detective Mattson's informant, our luck would finally change. We confirmed that the informant had received a load of cocaine from the stash house in Santa Clarita that Poncho visited. After learning this and noting it was nearly midnight, Detective Mattson had the team continue our surveillance of the stash house while he responded back to the station and completed his warrant. At 3:00 a.m., Detective Mattson, along with Sergeant Dalton and his crime impact team, were on scene at the stash house in Santa Clarita.

Detective Mattson called a meeting and told everyone he got a search warrant signed, and at 6:01 a.m., they'd serve the warrant on the stash house. Sergeant Tilly had Sergeant Dalton and his crime impact team hold the eye on the stash house, while the narcotic team tried to get a couple hours of sleep. Sergeant Tilly informed both teams we would reconvene at 5:30 a.m. to discuss responsibilities in executing the warrant.

Sergeant Dalton's crime impact team had five other members. The senior member, Detective Kevin Redmond, was small in stature, and had high-energy with a fun personality. Additionally, he was an outstanding investigator and was a well-respected liaison to the district attorney's office. Next was Detective Drew Prescott who had the complete opposite personality from Detective Redmond with his big, muscular physique and methodical approach to his decision-making. Detective Prescott, along with Sergeant Dalton were the team's experts in putting their entry plans together when executing search warrant entries and the take down of suspects.

Detective Mark Vaughn was a dedicated crime-fighter who had the reputation of a magnet when it came to finding the bad guys. Vaughn's toughness and no-nonsense personality made one feel safe when he was around. Detective Johnny Riggs was a former athlete and was considered the most well-rounded of the teammates with great investigation and surveillance skills. And finally, Detective Marty Caldwell was the youngest and newest member. He was built like a bull, which came in handy, as the crime impact team dealt with the worst of the worst felons.

At the 5:30 a.m. meeting, Detective Mattson told everyone to suit up and put on their raid gear, which included tactical bulletproof vests, Colt .45 sidearms, and one pistol grip sawed-off shotgun. The crime impact team would be responsible for the entry team. The reason was twofold; one, the narcotic team had been up for days with very little sleep, and two, the crime impact team performed more tactical entries than the narcotic team, and was more proficient in doing them. The narcotic team would be responsible for the outside perimeter in case someone tried to escape through the back of the house.

At 5:55 a.m., both teams moved in on the stash house, with Detective Mattson taking the eye. The crime impact team approached the front of the house with Sergeant Dalton coordinating both teams into positions. Once the narcotic team had the outside perimeter covered, Sergeant Dalton and his crime impact team approached the front door.

Detective Caldwell moved up, knocked on the door and identified himself as a police officer with a search warrant for the premises, and ordered the occupants inside to open the door. No response or movement was heard from inside the house. This all happened in a matter of seconds, but seemed forever. This was the most dangerous part of the entry because too much hesitation on our entry gave the bad guys time to arm themselves and shoot us as we entered the house.

Sergeant Dalton, taking all this in, nodded at Detective Prescott to take the door. Detective Prescott then took a steel ram, that weighed about seventy pounds, and slammed it into the door frame, knocking the door right off its hinges. Simultaneously, Detective Vaughn, with his pistol grip sawed-off shotgun, entered with Detective Redmond, Sergeant Dalton, and Detectives Riggs, Caldwell, Prescott in a line right behind.

Within a few seconds, Detective Vaughn encountered a person running out from a bedroom. He caught the guy with a right elbow to the chin, knocking him off his feet. Detective Redmond and the rest of the team stepped over them and continued searching the house. Detective Riggs found a second Latino hiding in the cabinet underneath the bathroom sink. Once the entire stash house was searched and cleared of any other occupants, Sergeant Dalton made an all-clear broadcast.

Sergeant Tilly and his narcotic team entered the house and searched for contraband. It was their case and their responsibility to search and gather as much evidence for the prosecution and for possible leads for further cases. Going through the evidence was critical and had to be done thoroughly and methodically—a tiring task especially when team members were operating with very little sleep.

While searching the house, the narcotic team located a false floor covered by a piece of carpet in the same bedroom that one of the bad guys ran out of. Inside they discovered nearly a ton of cocaine. While the narcotic team was happy, they knew their work had just begun.

Detective Mattson gave both teams addresses for two additional residences to be searched. He gave Sergeant Dalton the address to the potential stash pad in Culver City and sent me, as the lead, with the crime impact team to execute the warrant. He told the narcotic team to go to Poncho's house in Pacoima and serve the final warrant there.

Immediately, everyone dispersed to their respected locations to serve their warrants. The local police were requested and arrived on the scene in Santa Clarita. They helped secure the stash house while Detectives Mattson and Sears processed the kilos of cocaine.

Sergeant Dalton, the crime impact team, and I arrived at the Culver City apartment. Since I was familiar with the apartment, I walked by in my street clothes to scout it out. I looked for any movement or lights on inside. I took note of the layout and it appeared that either no one was there, or they were still sleeping. I quickly drew a diagram of the layout and gave it to Sergeant Dalton.

As I suited back up into my entry vest, Sergeant Dalton gave his team their assignment to enter the apartment. It was now 8:30 a.m., so if anyone was in the apartment, the element of surprise wouldn't be the same as before. Sergeant Dalton told me to take a position at the rear of the apartment, which was on the bottom floor with a back door leading to an alley.

As I got into position, the crime impact team approached the front door, then knocked and identified themselves. No one came to the door. Detective Prescott used his ram, knocked the front door down, and the team entered. As the team leapfrogged past one another checking bedrooms for occupants, Sergeant Dalton confronted a male in the second bedroom and quickly contained him at gunpoint. Detective Riggs saw a second male run out the back door where I was waiting. When he saw me, the male suspect stopped in his tracks as I held him at gunpoint. Detectives Riggs and Caldwell came out and put the suspect in handcuffs.

The apartment was deemed safe, with both males in handcuffs sitting on the living room floor. Neither male spoke much English, but Detective Vaughn spoke Spanish. The two males would only say that the apartment wasn't theirs and they were just spending the night. When pressed for more information, they both stopped talking. With the exception of two sleeping bags and a couch, the apartment was bare. Everything indicated that this was a typical stash house and these two Latinos were mule-level drug cartel members hired to watch the place.

The crime impact team and I searched the house. As we searched, Sergeant Dalton and I briefly stopped and sat down on the couch next to the two suspects. We began to talk to the suspects when Sergeant Dalton and I heard a noise coming from the couch we were sitting on. We both stood up in unison as we looked at each other. Sergeant Dalton removed the cushions on the couch and noticed it had a fold up bed inside. He pulled on the strap to open the bed and as it unfolded, we found a Latina inside. We couldn't believe it! We got her to her feet, handcuffed her, and placed her on the floor next to the other two. We then continued our search of the rest of the house. Initially we found no evidence of drug dealing, but I did one last walk-through to double-check. In the third bedroom, I noticed fresh paint on the back wall inside of the closet. Two small ropes protruded from small holes on each side of the wall. I asked Detective Redmond to pull on one rope while I pulled on the other. As we pulled, the entire back of the closet wall opened, revealing a large compartment.

What we saw next blew our minds—stacks upon stacks of US currency filled the entire compartment. Sergeant Dalton immediately took control of the scene. We processed the evidence, took pictures of everything, loaded the money in locked containers, and placed everything in Sergeant Dalton's car. We then returned to the Torrance Police station with the money and the three arrestees.

Sergeant Tilly and the narcotic team executed their search warrant on Poncho's house. The search came up empty for any cocaine or money, but the detectives did discover pay-and-owe sheets. Pay-and-owe sheets are records kept by drug organizations that show who purchased cocaine or marijuana from them, and which clients owed them money. Sergeant Tilly and his team returned to the Torrance Police Department with their evidence and with the arrestee, Poncho.

Because the Torrance Police Department only had one money counter, Lieutenant Pagh said there was so much money recovered from the Culver City stash pad that it had to be transported to a local Bank of America and be counted there. Sergeant Dalton and his crime impact team escorted Lieutenant Pagh, Sergeant Tilly, and Detective Mattson to the Bank of America nearby. Even with the money counters from the bank and the bank employees assisting, it still took several hours to count and double-count the money confiscated.

The total amount of drug money recovered? $1.2 million. For the most part, all confiscated money was considered asset forfeiture and would eventually come back to the city of Torrance. Lieutenant Pagh was very good at getting millions of dollars from drug cases back into the Torrance Police's crime-fighting funds.

CHAPTER
25

Three days later, Sergeant Tilly and our narcotic team were back at it and on another case—a spin-off from a previous case. The narcotic team was sitting on a house in Mission Viejo, California. Like most other cases, this included a long commute. A one-way trip to Mission Viejo was about an hour and a half drive for most of the team members.

The narcotic team had received information that Edgar Robles, who lived at this house, was a drug cartel member. Edgar was easy to identify; he was a forty-five-year-old Latino with salt-and-pepper hair, light-colored skin, and was six foot three. He was a flashy guy who wore gold necklaces and a Rolex watch. Edgar's daily routine was typical of a drug cartel member. He didn't appear to work and used pay phones to page and call people, instead of using a housephone.

It was the start of our second week of surveilling Edgar. In the first week, we surveilled him as he met up with several individuals for lunch and dinner. Edgar didn't drive in an anti-surveillance manner when meeting these people. One day, he left his house at 8:00 a.m. in his blue BMW. We followed him to the city of Yorba Linda, where he made some phone calls or pages. About thirty minutes later, he got back into his BMW and entered the 91 Freeway, heading west.

We continued to follow Edgar as he transitioned to the I-405 north. We noted no anti-surveillance driving at this time. He continued on the I-405 as he passed Culver City. Edgar was traveling in the number one lane, the fast lane, when he suddenly crossed all lanes and exited the Santa Monica off-ramp in West Los Angeles. When he reached the bottom of the off-ramp, he ran a red light, and turned right onto Santa Monica Boulevard, eastbound.

Detective Carroll was on point and calling the surveillance. Traffic was heavy, so we had several undercover cars out front and to the rear. While Edgar was using anti-surveillance driving, he wasn't overly aggressive, so it wasn't difficult following him. He continued eastbound as he entered the city of Beverly Hills. As he approached North Palm Drive, he quickly turned right without signaling.

Detective Carroll passed the surveillance call to Detective Mack, who had made the right turn on Palm Drive with Edgar and had a car in between them. Detective Mack called, "Edgar isn't looking in his mirrors too much, but it looks like he's dusting himself off. We're in a residential area with lots of apartments on both sides of the street. He just made a right turn into the alley behind the apartments on the north side of the street."

At that point, Detective Mack drove quickly to the west end of the alley, which let out onto a north-south street. As he drove past the entrance to the alley, he observed Edgar's BMW stationary about midblock in the alley. The team set up on both ends of the alley. Five minutes passed. Edgar then drove out of the west end of the alley. Detective Mack continued to call the surveillance and said, "Edgar made a right out of the alley—he is northbound on Alden Avenue heading back toward Santa Monica Boulevard."

Edgar reached Santa Monica Boulevard and made a left turn back toward the freeway. Detective Sears took over the surveillance and broadcast, "Edgar now has a male passenger in his BMW. I didn't get a good look at him, but he appears to be a large male."

The narcotic team surveilled Edgar and his passenger back to the I-405. While the team followed him, Detective Mack returned to the alley where Edgar had parked. He wrote down the address, noting that four small apartments were at this address—two upstairs and two downstairs.

Detective Sears handed off the point to me as we surveilled Edgar back onto the I-405 southbound. It was about noon and traffic was heavy. We continued following Edgar south on the I-405 as he moved over to the slow lane. When Edgar approached Century Boulevard, he exited and stopped at the red light at the bottom of the off-ramp. Although there was lots of traffic, the entire narcotic team managed to take the off-ramp with him.

Sergeant Tilly took over the point. When the light turned green, Edgar turned left and headed east on Century Boulevard. Detective Carroll drove out front in case Edgar made it through a traffic signal and the rest of us got stuck behind. The narcotic team couldn't figure out why Edgar would be driving in the crime-plagued part of the city of Inglewood, especially in his BMW wearing his flashy jewelry. As Edgar approached Prairie Avenue, everyone finally realized why. He was going to Hollywood Park Racetrack. When Edgar drove into the lot and parked, the narcotic team proceeded to do the same.

Sergeant Tilly told Detective Mack and I to follow Edgar and his passenger into the racetrack to see if they were meeting up with anyone. We stood in line to enter, standing two people back from them. The new Latino looked like he could be a brother, if not a twin, to Edgar. The only difference was Edgar had salt-and-pepper hair and his was black, and Edgar was about an inch taller.

Although it was midweek, the racetrack was busy, so it was easy to blend in. Detective Mack and I bought programs and racing forms as we watched Edgar and his passenger closely. They seemed right at home. They bought racing forms and paid for really nice seats in an upper-level restaurant directly above the finish line. Edgar and his companion sat a table with four chairs and had a waiter to serve them.

They walked to the windows to make a bet, so I followed behind to make a bet myself. Of course, I had to fit in! I was close enough to hear them as they placed a hundred-dollar bet on the number four horse to win. Both spoke English but with a heavy Latino accent.

I followed their lead and bet ten dollars to place and show on the same number four horse. Then I made my way back to Detective Mack, who was situated several tables over from Edgar and his passenger. I handed Mack my betting slip, "You owe me ten bucks." He reluctantly pulled out his wallet and gave me ten, laughing.

Before the race went off, I headed to a secluded hallway and used my portable radio to contact Sergeant Tilly and the team. After I reported what was going on, I could hear numerous jokes about us gambling on duty. I told Sergeant Tilly that I'd give updates when I could and to page me if he needed me.

When I walked back to my table, I noticed a beautiful Latina in her late twenties or early thirties, along with a thin Latino about the same age, sitting with Edgar and his passenger. Detective Mack, pretending to discuss the racing form with me, whispered that the thin Latino was the same guy in the leather jacket from Jack's Burgers who met with Poncho. The beautiful female was doing most of the talking with hand gestures directed at Edgar and his passenger. Mack and I agreed that these two new players were heavy hitters, and we should bed them down to see where they lived.

Mack said, "Since you're back now, I'm going to contact Sergeant Tilly and the team and tell them about our plan." When Mack left the table, the race went off. I noted that Edgar and his three guests stopped talking to watch, but it didn't appear that the Latina and her male companion were at all interested, as they began talking again.

When the race concluded, they said goodbye to Edgar in Spanish and left. I remained seated, keeping an eye on Edgar and his passenger. Some time had passed, and I hadn't received a page from Sergeant Tilly or heard from Mack telling me they were following the new female and her Latino companion. I was beginning to get worried. The last time I saw Mack, he was walking around the corner into the hallway to use his portable radio.

Five, ten, and then fifteen minutes went by. Now I was really concerned about where Detective Mack was and if he'd made contact with the narcotic team outside. I didn't want Sergeant Tilly and the team to miss these new players when they exited the track—again, they looked like major players within the organization. I finally got up to look for him.

As I rounded the hallway, I saw four plain-clothed track security personnel pressing Mack up against the wall. He was handcuffed. I couldn't believe it! I rushed over and identified myself. These bozos looked at me, looked at my badge, and said to one another, "Maybe this one's telling the truth. Maybe they are cops." Security had watched Mack on their security cameras while he was talking on a portable radio. They also saw his gun in his waistband.

I yelled at Mack, "Why didn't you identify yourself as a cop?"

"I did! But these guys didn't give me a chance to show my badge and ID! They told me to shut up and slapped these cuffs on me!"

"Did you notify the team about the new players and our plan to watch them?"

"No. How could I?"

I couldn't believe what was happening. I told the four security guys to uncuff Mack and looked around the corner to make sure Edgar and his passenger were still at their table. Both were up at the windows making another bet. I radioed Sergeant Tilly and the team about the meeting between Edgar, the new Latina, and the skinny Latino—the same Latino who met up with Poncho prior to his cocaine delivery. Sergeant Tilly said, "We've been watching the exit, but there are hundreds of people here, so we didn't notice those two."

I gave the narcotic team a detailed description of the two drug cartel members and reminded them that the skinny Latino was last seen driving a beige Nissan. Sergeant Tilly radioed to Detective Carroll, who was watching the front gate, and asked if he had seen a beige Nissan with our players in it. Carroll responded, "No, but I wasn't looking for it because I didn't get their description."

We were all frustrated. Once again, we failed to follow and identify the skinny Latino or the new Latina. There was a good chance that the Latina was the one our informant said was in charge. The information we kept getting from our sources indicated that a pretty female drug cartel member was in charge of the entire Cali Drug Cartel organization in the Western United States, and we just blew an opportunity to follow her!

Drug cartel organizations rarely gave you an opportunity to identify the higher-ranking members. They're very elusive with many layers of workers beneath them shielding them from law enforcement. Because the higher-ups rarely showed up in Southern California, it was nearly impossible to get enough evidence to indict and prosecute them.

I informed Sergeant Tilly that I'd debrief the security personnel who had detained Detective Mack and find out what I could about Edgar and his passenger. It seemed to me that Edgar was a regular gambler here. I asked the four security personnel, "Can you have your head of security or manager come speak with us?"

Detective Mack said, "I'll talk to the manager and you keep an eye on Edgar and his passenger. You look more like a regular here than I do."

This was true, as Detective Riggs, from the crime impact team, and I liked to go to the races once in a while in our downtime. Mack then added, "Here, you can have this too." And he handed over the betting slip I gave him earlier.

I returned to my seat and watched Edgar and his passenger studying their racing forms. Keeping an eye on them, I went to the betting window to see if I had won anything on the last race, and lo and behold, I won eighty bucks. I backed away from the window and stood nearby, and watched Edgar approach the window again.

This time he placed a three-hundred-dollar bet on the number eight horse. Again, I followed his lead and bet ten dollars to win and place on the same horse. I was amazed by the amount of money Edgar was betting, obviously a benefit of being involved in the drug business. The next race went off, and the number eight horse came in dead last! I guess Edgar wasn't much of a horseplayer after all. A good handicapper wouldn't spend three hundred dollars on a horse that came in last place.

Forty-five minutes later, Detective Mack returned to update me. "First," he said, "the security supervisor was an off-duty LAPD cop, and he apologized for the mix-up. When they saw me using my portable on their security cameras, they thought I was talking to a bookie."

"Anyway," Detective Mack said, "he gave me the lowdown on Edgar and his passenger. Apparently, Edgar is a regular at the track here, as well as the Santa Anita and Del Mar racetracks. The other guy is his twin brother, Daniel Robles, and they both bet big. That's about all they know about them. Otherwise, they keep to themselves and don't cause any trouble. Today was the first time they've seen

Edgar and Daniel meet with anyone, and they have never seen the female or male before."

Detective Mack continued, "The supervisor said he's in the process of downloading the security camera pictures of the pretty female and skinny male. He said if we're still here, he'll give them to us. Otherwise, he'll have one of his guys drop the photographs off at the station in an envelope with my name on it."

As we spoke, Edgar and Daniel started walking toward the escalator that led to the exit. I radioed the team to let them know that they were on their way out. The team followed them to Daniel's apartment in Beverly Hills. Edgar drove in a normal manner until he was close to Daniel's apartment. Then he drove around the block a few times, looking for a tail. While he was doing that, Detective Sears got out on foot. When Edgar dropped Daniel off, he saw the apartment Daniel entered.

The team then followed Edgar back to his home in Mission Viejo. It was about 8:00 p.m., and we decided to call it a night. We agreed we needed to continue to surveil Edgar and hoped he'd meet up with the pretty Latina or the skinny Latino from the track again. We knew the skinny Latino met with Poncho before the previous shipment of cocaine came in. We also knew Poncho told our informant that although he'd never met the pretty Latina who was supposedly in charge in Southern California, he'd seen her once, and he said she was young and very pretty.

From our intelligence information, along with Poncho's information, we were sure that the pretty young Latina from the racetrack was the same one responsible for most of the cocaine smuggling into Western United States. We had to find her again, or at least find the skinny Latino who was with her. We started referring to the skinny Latino as "the secretary" to the pretty Latina. We all agreed to begin surveilling Edgar's house the next morning at eight o'clock.

As it turned out, our hopes were dashed. For the next three weeks, we surveilled Edgar's house and followed him from San Diego to Beverly Hills and to the racetrack. He met with several people, including his brother, but nothing worthwhile occurred. Did I mention that it took a lot of persistence to be a good detective?

CHAPTER
26

We had been following Edgar for four months now with no significant activity. One day we surveilled him to the city of Santa Ana. As we followed him, he started driving in an anti-surveillance manner. He ran a few red traffic lights, pulled over and let traffic pass him, all while constantly looking in his rearview and side mirrors. When he felt he wasn't being followed, he drove into a go-cart business. The go-carts were actually racing go-carts that people raced professionally.

When Edgar entered the business, Detective Carroll followed him. Detective Carroll observed Edgar walk into an employee-only area and enter an office. As Detective Carroll watched the people racing around a half-mile track, he started up a conversation with one of the employees. The employee explained, "These go-carts are high-end performance race cars driven by professional drivers who are sponsored and race for money. There's a racing circuit around the world. The drivers and their owners are a tight-knit community."

Detective Carroll also learned that the racetrack was owned by a family from Santa Ana and that it was a very expensive sport. Only the wealthy could afford to be involved. The employee said the Sousa family, who were originally from South America, owned the track. The Sousa's had two sons who were well-known champions in the sport and the family competed all over the world, including South America.

The employee asked Detective Carroll, "Are you going out on the track today?"

"Maybe next time. I'm just checking it out today—seeing how much it costs. Next time, I'll come back with a few friends and we'll give it a go."

Detective Carroll then wandered over to the office area, but all he could see was a hallway with many offices. He couldn't tell which office Edgar had gone into.

Before leaving, Detective Carroll grabbed some pricing information from the counter. As he walked out, he could see security cameras overlooking the entire parking lot. He got back to his car, bent over like he was grabbing something from the floorboard, and radioed the team, "There are cameras all over. Everyone needs to leave the lot."

Detective Sears was already across the street with an eye on the front entrance—the only way to enter or exit the business. Detective Carroll found a vacant parking lot nearby and told the rest of team to meet him there.

Detective Carroll updated the team about the South American owners, the Sousa's, and how he had watched Edgar enter the employee-only area and disappear into a back office. Everyone was thinking the same thing; the business was a front for importing cocaine for the drug cartels. Sergeant Tilly commented, "They're probably laundering money for the drug cartels too."

The question before the team was, who should we follow? Should we try and identify the owners and surveil them, or should we continue to follow Edgar in hopes that he'd set up a possible cocaine or money deal? We decided to continue surveilling Edgar while finding out all we could about the go-cart racing business.

Suddenly, Detective Sears broadcast, "Edgar is walking back to his car." We rushed to our cars and "starburst out" to follow Edgar. Edgar exited the parking lot and drove about a mile down the street to a bank of pay phones. He parked and appeared to make several pages and phone calls for about forty-five minutes. When he was done, Edgar drove back to his house in Mission Viejo. We surveilled his home until about 10:00 p.m., until the house lights went out, and we called it a night.

*****

Several weeks passed with no significant activity. One morning, I got to Edgar's house early—about 7:00 a.m. because I was tired of getting stuck in traffic, so I left early to avoid it. I grabbed a cup of coffee and took the eye watching Edgar's house. At 7:20, Edgar's garage door opened, and he drove out. This was so unexpected and I was the only one on scene.

I broadcast to the team, "Edgar is mobile in his BMW!" Everyone replied that they were at least thirty minutes out. I told them I'd call the surveillance but wouldn't do anything stupid to get burned by him.

Edgar drove to a gas station and filled his tank. He then drove to a pay phone in the gas station parking lot and used it. I was hoping that this would give the team time to catch up. Edgar used the phone for about fifteen minutes, then got back into his car and left the parking lot. I followed him as he got onto the I-5 north.

Traffic was horrible, and I was having a hard time keeping Edgar in my view. I was finally able to get two cars behind him in the number two lane; the second lane from the fast lane. The narcotic team members were copying my broadcast, and all got off the southbound side of the I-5 and jumped back onto the I-5 north. As long as Edgar didn't switch lanes and other motorists didn't get between the two cars in front of me, I knew I'd be okay.

Finally, Sergeant Tilly caught up with me, and not long after, everyone else did too. The team chattered about the time Edgar left this morning—much earlier than usual. Because he changed his normal pattern, everyone was optimistic that things were heating up. After four months on the case, the team was getting tired of nothing happening.

Edgar continued on the I-5 north to the I-405, where he headed north. He approached the 22 Freeway and entered eastbound toward the city of Santa Ana. As we entered the city of Garden Grove, he suddenly switched lanes and cut off several drivers as he approached the Euclid off-ramp. We had plenty of time to position ourselves in case Edgar exited the freeway. I was still calling the surveillance and was one lane to Edgar's left. As he approached the Euclid off-ramp, it looked like he was going to pass it, but at the last second, he whamboed onto it and cut off several cars. The narcotic team was in position and exited the freeway with Edgar.

Detective Sears took over the call of Edgar, as I couldn't exit the off-ramp. I pulled over to the shoulder and when I heard Detective Sears call Edgar down the off-ramp and out of my view, I four-wheeled down the embankment onto the off-ramp. Many motorists were cussing at me. I got to the red light at the bottom and traffic was clear, so I ran the red light and sped to catch up.

Detective Sears continued to broadcast the direction of Edgar's travel. He and the team followed him southbound Euclid Street, until he suddenly pulled over and parked his car. As Sergeant Tilly passed him, he said, "It looks like Edgar's watching who's passing him."

I was far enough back, so I was able to pull over and watch Edgar's movements. Everyone else had to drive past him. Because the streets were very busy, we weren't afraid Edgar had burned our surveillance.

Edgar went mobile again, continuing southbound on Euclid, and I began calling the surveillance. He came upon a small residential street and made a quick left turn. As I approached the street he had driven down, I broadcast, "He's driving slowly eastbound on Sixteenth Street." I turned right, went the opposite direction, and called Edgar's actions in my rearview mirror. Edgar then turned left on the first north-south street he came to, out of my view.

Detective Carroll came on the air and broadcast, "I have Edgar northbound on La Bonita Street." He followed Edgar for one block to Westminster Boulevard, where Edgar pulled into a McDonald's parking lot. As Detective Carroll drove past the McDonald's, he saw that Edgar was out of his car and walking into McDonald's. Detective Mack drove into the parking lot, advised that he'd be off the air, and went inside.

As Detective Mack entered, he saw Edgar at a table overlooking Westminster Boulevard. Acting like a customer, Detective Mack stood in line, ordered some food, and sat at a table that gave him a clear view of Edgar.

Ten minutes later, two short Latinos walked in and looked around. When they saw Edgar, they walked over to him and sat down at his table. Detective Mack noticed Edgar shaking their hands. Edgar appeared to do all the talking. At one point, he took out a white paper bag from his jacket pocket and slid it to the older, heavier Latino. The heavy Latino wore a long-sleeved dark blue shirt while the other younger Latino wore a short-sleeved red t-shirt. Detective Mack couldn't see what was in the bag, but noticed it was three to four inches thick.

After ten minutes, Edgar stood up from the table, followed by the two Latinos. All three exited McDonald's through the north exit. Detective Mack quickly walked out the east exit doors, shielding himself as he got on his radio to let the narcotic team know what he had observed. He also gave descriptions of the two new players. Sergeant Tilly, who was on the eye and watching Edgar's car, broadcast, "All three just entered Edgar's car."

Edgar drove out of the parking lot eastbound on Westminster Boulevard. Sergeant Tilly controlled the radio discussion and called the surveillance of Edgar's car. Sergeant Tilly pressed Detective Mack on the size of the bag Edgar had given to the older Latino with the dark blue shirt. Detective Mack said, "It was no bigger than a lunch bag, and it contained nothing larger than four inches thick. Based on prior cases, it could be traveling expenses for the two new mules in Edgar's car."

Sergeant Tilly continued to call the surveillance of Edgar eastbound Westminster Boulevard. He asked Detective Mattson, the case agent, "Who do you want us to follow if Edgar drops these two new guys off somewhere?"

Detective Mattson, without hesitation, said, "Lets follow the two new guys."

I laughed, and I was sure everyone else laughed too because if Detective Mattson had said to follow Edgar, everyone would have gone ballistic! These two mules were going to be the hands-on guys, and Edgar was going to reap the benefits. Hopefully that wouldn't happen, and we would be able to tie Edgar to this case when it culminated and we made arrests.

We followed Edgar's car back to the Santa Ana go-cart racetrack. The racetrack appeared to be closed, but Edgar drove in anyway. Knowing there were cameras overlooking the parking lot, the narcotic team stayed clear. Detective Mattson had the eye on the front entrance/exit. Using binoculars, he could see all three getting out of Edgar's car and walking to the north side of the building, out of his view. Mattson asked, "Can anyone get over to the north side of the parking lot to see what's going on?"

I was able to find some high ground that gave me a great view. Using binoculars, I could see over a large fence that surrounded the racetrack business. I broadcast, "I can see our three players in a large service—or warehouse area. It looks like they work on the go-carts in there. I can see that the older Latino with the long-sleeved dark blue shirt still has the white paper bag in his right rear pocket."

As I was broadcasting, Detective Mattson said, "A large semitruck just pulled into the parking lot. It's heading toward the north side of the building."

I called, "The semitruck just pulled up to the big service area. It's backing up into the service bay." As the semitruck backed into the service bay, the roll door shut behind it. Detective Mattson asked Detective Sears to take his position with the eye on the front entrance while he talked the case over with Sergeant Tilly. I still had the eye on the closed service door.

After two hours, there was still no movement on my side of the building. The business was open now and patrons had entered using the front entrance.

Detective Sears had the eye on the front of the building and broadcast, "Edgar just exited the building and is walking toward his car alone."

Mattson replied, "Let Edgar go. We'll surveil the two new guys. Detective Carroll, you loosely follow Edgar away from the area to make sure he doesn't double back and counter-surveil us." When Edgar left the parking lot, Detective Carroll followed him and watched him enter the 22 Freeway westbound. Detective Carroll let Edgar go and returned to our location.

As I watched the service bay, I pulled out my 300mm surveillance camera and stood ready in case I was able to get some photos. Suddenly the roll door opened, and the older Latino with the dark blue shirt appeared in front of the semitruck with a tall Latino I hadn't seen before. I took photos of them talking and shaking hands. The Latino with the dark blue shirt got into the driver's side of the semitruck and closed the door. I broadcast to the team, "The younger Latino wearing the red shirt just appeared, opened the passenger door of the semitruck, entered, and sat down." Detective Mattson told us we were going to surveil the semitruck when it left.

"The truck is starting up," I radioed. Shortly after, the semitruck with our two mules—the Latino in the long-sleeved dark blue shirt and the Latino in the red shirt—drove out of the service bay and exited the parking lot. Detective Sears took over the call and called the truck out of the parking lot. Since we were following a semitruck, we would have no problem losing sight of it.

Detective Mack drove out front of the semitruck and using his rearview mirror, confirmed, "The driver is the same older Latino with the long-sleeved dark blue shirt that Edgar had passed the white paper bag to in McDonald's. And the passenger is the younger Latino with the short-sleeved red shirt. I can see both players smiling and carrying on a conversation."

The Santa Ana Freeway was coming up. Detective Mack passed underneath the freeway and continued to call the semitruck onto the Santa Ana Freeway south. Sergeant Tilly took over the call and confirmed the semitruck was southbound on the Santa Ana Freeway in the slow lane. Traffic was moderate, and the surveillance team stayed way behind in the slow lane.

Detective Mattson asked, "Are these guys going to Mexico?"

Sergeant Tilly, who was still on the point, replied, "That's certainly a possibility."

The narcotic team followed the semitruck onto the 55 Freeway westbound, then onto the I-405 southbound. Following a big, slow semitruck was easy but boring. Sergeant Tilly needed a break, so I took over the call. Detective Mattson came on air and said, "Looks like this vehicle is registered to a trucking company in Del Rio, Texas."

We continued southbound driving slowly at 55 mph on the I-405 through the city of Irvine. As we approached the I-5 transition, the semitruck continued going south, toward San Diego. I needed a break, so Detective Sears took over the surveillance call.

As seasoned detectives, we were all prepared for long, slow surveillances. During a surveillance, you couldn't afford to lose anyone for any kind of break, even a bathroom break. So, we all carried portable hospital urinals in our undercover cars. It was just part of the job!

As we slowly headed south on the I-5, we passed Camp Pendleton, the marine base. Sergeant Tilly discussed our plan if they continued into Mexico. We had a few options. One, we could notify officials from the American border patrol, which was controlled by the El Paso Intelligence Center (EPIC). EPIC is run by the Drug Enforcement Agency (DEA) and assists state and federal agencies with intelligence information about vehicles and individuals coming in and out of our southern borders. But this wasn't a great option because we all believed the truck was empty and was headed to Mexico to pick up a load of cocaine.

The second option was to let the two Latinos drive into Mexico and wait for them to come back. The downside of this scenario is that it could be months before we see them come back into the United States—and only if they came back through the San Diego border. There were plenty of other ways to return to the United States with multiple border entries in California, Arizona, or even Texas. Because the truck was registered in Del Rio, Texas, it was definitely an option they might choose.

Third, we could notify our border patrol to put a hit on the license plate in EPIC's database, so they could notify us if and when it crossed back into the United States. This was a gamble, as our border patrol officers would have to talk to Mexican officials. From past experiences at the border, we knew some Mexican officials were corrupt and couldn't be trusted. We also knew we couldn't follow them into Mexico, as we had no law enforcement powers there.

After much discussion, we agreed to let the semitruck go into Mexico. We would notify EPIC and have them put the semitruck's data in their system, so when the truck crossed back into the United States at any crossing, we would be notified. We would also ask that they do nothing more than their normal routine of identifying the occupants and inquiring about the transportation manifest.

If by chance they came back through the San Diego crossing, we would have a chance of returning there to surveil it. Detective Carroll lived in northeast San Diego and could quickly get to the border and follow the semitruck. This would give the rest of us time to get down to the border and catch up with Detective Carroll.

In many drug smuggling cases, the semitrucks had sophisticated secret compartments built into them. The secret compartments were so well concealed that they often went undetected by the border patrol agents, and tons of cocaine was smuggled into the United States. In this case, we were willing to take our chances by notifying the border officials, hoping that the semitruck would come back through the San Diego border.

Ideally, we wanted to follow the semitruck to whatever city they were going to and close the case with arrests and cocaine seizures. But in reality, we only had one option—to get EPIC officials involved. If the semitruck came back through the border and the border patrol agents discovered cocaine, at least a large amount of cocaine would be confiscated before it hit the streets in the United States.

As the semitruck approached the border, Sergeant Tilly told Detectives Mattson and Mack to contact EPIC officials. The team convened in a border patrol parking lot while Detectives Mattson and Mack went inside the building. While we waited, we stretched our legs and ate lunch.

Thirty minutes later, Detective Mattson told us that EPIC had all the information in their database. If and when the semitruck came back through the border, we would be notified immediately. Our mission for the day was now accomplished, and we made the long drive home.

CHAPTER
27

The next couple of weeks were quiet, so the team caught up on paperwork to develop other potential cases. Twice the team drove down to Mission Viejo and surveilled Edgar, but all he did was go to the racetrack.

Three more weeks went by before Detective Mattson was notified by the border patrol; our semitruck was at the San Diego border and was about to go through customs. Detective Mattson directed the narcotic team to get to the border. Detective Carroll, who lived in San Diego and had the day off, was the first to head down.

Detective Mattson told the border patrol supervisor to take their time in processing the semitruck. The supervisor said, "If we find any contraband, we'll follow protocol and arrest and seize whatever we find."

Mattson replied, "That's fine, but we want to interview anyone you've arrested."

Detective Carroll arrived at the border within an hour and set up surveillance of the semitruck. He identified himself to the supervisor in charge and asked if they had discovered anything in the semitruck. The supervisor said, "Our drug dogs had a hit on the truck, but they couldn't find any illegal drugs." He gave Detective Carroll a printout of the personal information about the two occupants of the semitruck.

Detective Carroll recognized the description of the occupants as the same two we followed down to the border nearly six weeks ago. The manifest and a search by the border patrol officers showed that the truck contained racing go-carts and parts going to the Santa Ana go-cart business. Once the border patrol agents were done with their investigation, they waved the semitruck through.

Detective Carroll radioed the team about the release of the truck and told us it was headed northbound on the I-5. The team got off the freeway and positioned themselves to join in on the surveillance once the semitruck passed them. Twenty minutes later, the semitruck passed the team and Detective Carroll continued to call the surveillance of the slow-moving semitruck. He advised, "The border patrol officers said their drug dogs had a hit on the truck for contraband, but they didn't find anything during their search."

The fact that the border patrol's drug-sniffing dogs had a hit meant there was a good possibility the semitruck was carrying cocaine in a secret compartment that border patrol agents missed. Detective Carroll told the team, "The same two Latinos are in the semitruck. Both are wearing the same clothes as before. The truck is carrying racing go-carts and parts. Everything indicates that the occupants work for the go-cart business in Santa Ana, and they're driving the truck back there."

I took over calling surveillance for Detective Carroll, so he could get some rest. We were going 55 mph and passing the San Onofre power plant, still northbound on the I-5. We approached the I-5 and I-405 split, and I figured the driver would take the I-405 as before. But instead, he exited Lake Forest Drive in the city of Lake Forest. This was definitely a surprise, and we didn't know what to make of it. We just knew we had to be on our A game.

We followed the semitruck to the bottom of the Lake Forest Drive off-ramp. The semitruck went straight on Lake Forest Drive, paralleling the freeway. I turned right, and Sergeant Tilly took over the surveillance call. When the semitruck turned right on Serrano Avenue, Sergeant Tilly continued straight and handed the call to Mack.

Detective Mack said, "We're in an industrial area with lots of warehouse buildings on both sides of the street. The truck just pulled into a large parking lot and is driving up to a warehouse." Detective Mack handed the call off to Detective Mattson, who pulled over and had a great view of the semitruck in the parking lot. I pulled my car around and positioned myself to get some surveillance pictures.

Detective Mattson broadcast, "The younger Latino with the red shirt just exited the passenger door and is walking to the large roll door of the warehouse. He's unlocking the roll door—But it looks like the door is too heavy for him to open. The older Latino in the long-sleeved dark blue shirt just got out of the truck and is helping him open the door. The driver got back into the truck and he's backing up. Now he's turning the truck around and backing into the warehouse." Once the semitruck pulled into the warehouse, both Latinos rolled down the door and were out of our view.

Detective Mattson commented over the radio, "Now this is interesting!" Why weren't these guys taking the go-carts to the race-track in Santa Ana? Our plan now was to wait. We still didn't know if there was any cocaine in the semitruck. The border patrol said there wasn't, so no laws had been broken. We had no reason to arrest or search anybody or take any action, so we would have to wait and see.

At this point, we all began to realize that this was going to be a long night. It was about 9:00 p.m. and getting cold. Everyone was exhausted. Detective Sears took over the eye on the warehouse, and I was watching the back door. Everyone else parked, grabbed blankets or sleeping bags, and got some shut-eye.

At 3:00 a.m., Detective Sears was still watching the front of the warehouse. Detective Mattson took my position watching the back door, and I parked and got some rest. Being narcotic cops, we all felt very comfortable sleeping in our undercover cars.

Morning and afternoon came and went with no movement from the warehouse. At 6:00 p.m., the roll door finally opened, and the young Latino in the red shirt drove out in a black Honda Civic. We saw the older Latino close the roll door behind him. Detective Sears was watching the front of the warehouse and Sergeant Tilly had the back door. The rest of team followed the black Honda as it drove away. Sergeant Tilly broadcast, "I called Sergeant Dalton. The crime impact team is on its way to help."

We were in an industrial area, so we had to be careful not to stand out. I was calling the surveillance of the Honda now, as it left the industrial area traveling back toward the I-5. The driver accelerated quickly, went underneath the freeway and made a sharp left turn. I made a right turn, calling the surveillance in my rearview mirror. Detective Mack took over the call and observed the driver stop for a red light, look both ways, and run the red light. At the very least, we knew the driver must be meeting someone important, as he was certainly checking for a tail.

When the Honda drove around a slight bend in the road, the four of us—Mattson, Carroll, Mack, and I—ran the red traffic light to catch up. We made the turn but lost sight of the Honda. We all began searching the area. When I spotted the driver at a pay phone in a 7-Eleven parking lot at Peachwood Avenue and Palmwood Drive, I noted that he wasn't looking around. He made a phone call, most likely to a pager, and hung up. He appeared to be waiting for a return call.

Sergeant Tilly was listening in and said, "Things are looking pretty good. Sergeant Dalton and his team are almost on scene." Detective Prescott from the crime impact team had already arrived, as he lived nearby in Lake Forest. He took over Sergeant Tilly's eye on the rear door of the warehouse, so he could join us as our player waited for a callback.

Twenty minutes later, our player answered the phone, talked no more than five minutes, and hung up. He returned to his Honda, appeared to scan the area, and then drove away. He picked up speed, drove two blocks, and made a quick right turn down a residential street. By the time we got there, he was making another right turn.

I asked, "Is anyone still at the 7-Eleven?"

"I am," confirmed Detective Mack.

"Stay put. I think our player is going around the block."

A few minutes later, there was still no sign of our player, so Sergeant Tilly slowly went around the block. As he did, he saw the Honda parked with our player still in the driver's seat.

Sergeant Tilly relayed, "Don't come down the street. Just cap off both ends."

I had a view of the Honda and was watching it with my binoculars. It was easy to spot because the driver kept stepping on the brake pedal, illuminating the brake lights.

Thirty minutes passed with no change. Detective Carroll commented, "After we culminate this case, we'll follow up and find out how long the warehouse has been rented for. It looks like this operation has been up and running for some time."

Detective Mack advised, "A dark blue panel van just pulled into the 7-Eleven parking lot. A Latino got out and is now on the pay phone. He must have called a pager because he dialed and hung up."

Five minutes later, our player wearing the red shirt in the black Honda pulled away from the curb and headed back towards the 7-Eleven.

Detective Mack broadcast, "Our player in the black Honda is inbound and pulling into the 7-Eleven parking lot. He parked and is now exiting his Honda. He's walking up to the Latino at the pay phone and they're talking. The new Latino from the van is young, maybe in his late twenties, and is wearing a light-green shirt with blue jeans. He just handed our player something. Our player is walking to the dark blue-panel van and is getting in the driver's seat. Our player in the red shirt is driving the van out of the 7-Eleven parking lot." Everyone followed except for Detective Mack, who stayed with the new player from the van.

Sergeant Dalton and the crime impact team were listening to what was happening, so they set up back at the warehouse. We followed our player in the red shirt driving the van. We noticed that he was driving erratically, so we gave him a lot of room. Clearly, he was looking for someone following him. Detective Mattson drove way out in front of the van and headed back toward the warehouse. When he was within a couple of blocks, he went the opposite way. Our player in the van entered the parking lot by himself.

Detective Sears, who was on the eye in front of the warehouse, called it, "The Latino in the red shirt got out of the van and is knocking on the roll door. The older Latino with the dark blue shirt is opening the roll door from inside the warehouse. The Latino in the red shirt got back in the van and is driving into the warehouse. The older Latino is closing the roll door."

Sergeant Tilly told everyone to sit tight while he'd discuss our next move with Detective Mattson. A short time later, Sergeant Tilly came on the radio and advised, "When the blue van leaves the warehouse, Sergeant Dalton and his crime impact team will stay at the warehouse and maintain surveillance. The narcotic team will follow the van back to the 7-Eleven."

Sergeant Tilly said, "We aren't sure if the van will have product in it since the border patrol's search came up empty. Detective Mattson is meeting with a local police officer in a black-and-white. He may be needed to make a traffic stop on the van after it's dropped off by our Latino with the red shirt. We'll make that call when we get to that point. Does anyone have any questions?" No one did, so we sat and waited.

Forty minutes later, the roll door opened and the blue panel van exited the warehouse. The same Latino wearing the red shirt was driving. We only had one guy—myself—following and calling the surveillance on the van. The rest of the team was out front, keeping out of sight. I was lying way back where I could see and call the van's movements.

The Latino was now driving the speed limit, not erratically like before. All signs indicated that the van now had product in it. As the van left the industrial neighborhood, I let it go and Detective Sears picked up the call. The van proceeded to the freeway, drove underneath it and back toward the 7-Eleven.

Detective Sears stayed back and handed the call over to Detective Carroll, who was out in front. Carroll called the surveillance through his rearview mirror. As he approached the 7-Eleven, he let Detective Mack, who was still on the eye, call the surveillance. Detective Mack said, "I've got the van inbound. The same young Latino in the red shirt is driving. He just pulled into the parking lot and parked."

The entire narcotic team immediately called out their positions to make sure all routes were covered. We wanted to be close if Detective Mattson's call was to take down the two Latinos in the

7-Eleven parking lot. Detective Mattson came on air and said, "Let the two Latinos switch cars, then follow the Latino in the van. Once the van is out of view of the Latino in the Honda, the local black-and-white will make a traffic stop on the van, and we'll go from there."

Detective Mattson asked Sergeant Dalton and his crime impact team to respond to the 7-Eleven to surveil the black Honda back to the warehouse. Sergeant Dalton replied, "Copy that. Detectives Riggs and Caldwell, you stay at the warehouse." The crime impact team responded to the 7-Eleven and the Latino in the red shirt got out of the van, walked up to the new Latino, and returned the key to his van. The new Latino then got in his van and exited the 7-Eleven parking lot toward the I-5.

The Latino in the red shirt returned to his black Honda, also exited the parking lot, and appeared to be driving back to the warehouse. Sergeant Dalton and his team loosely followed the Honda to the warehouse. Detective Riggs, had the eye on the front of the warehouse and called, "The black Honda just pulled into the parking lot and up to the roll door. The driver got out and he's knocking on the roll door." Moments later, the same older Latino opened the roll door, and the Latino in the red shirt got into the black Honda and drove into the warehouse. The roll door closed behind them.

While this was going on, the narcotic team was surveilling the dark blue panel van potentially carrying a load of cocaine. After observing the anti-surveillance driving and car switch, it looked like a classic dope deal was going down, and we felt we needed to stop the van.

Detective Carroll was on the eye as we followed the van onto the I-5 south. Detective Mattson, who was with the local police officer in his black-and-white, told him we wanted him to make a traffic stop on the van. Detective Carroll announced, "The van just signaled and is exiting the freeway at Crown Valley off-ramp in Mission Viejo. I'll be out in front of the van, calling it. Detective Mattson, have the black-and-white make a traffic stop at the bottom of the off-ramp. I'll be in front of the van so it can't flee."

As the van exited the Crown Valley off-ramp, the black-and-white quickly came up behind the van, turned on its overhead light bar, and initiated a traffic stop. The rest of the narcotic team followed behind. When the van stopped, Detective Carroll stopped too. He quickly backed his undercover car's rear bumper into the van's front bumper, a technique we used so the van couldn't flee.

Suddenly, the van's driver opened the door and took off running. The police officer just exiting his car was stunned. I quickly drove past the traffic stop, passing the driver of the van who continued running. I stopped, jumped out of my car, and pointed my Colt .45 at the fleeing driver.

The driver didn't see me at first as he was looking back at the police officer. He suddenly turned around and saw me five feet away with a gun pointed at his head. Without hesitation, he threw his hands in the air and gave up. Detective Carroll arrived to handcuff and search him.

Sergeant Tilly and Detective Mattson were also at the traffic stop. When they looked in the van through the open door, they saw hundreds of kilos of cocaine wrapped in green-colored bundles. Mattson looked at the rest of us and said, "We hit the jackpot!"

Sergeant Tilly let Sergeant Dalton know that cocaine was found in the van and asked him to stop and detain anyone who came out of the warehouse until a search warrant could be obtained. Detective Mattson immediately went to the Lake Forest Police Department to update his warrant and get it signed by a judge.

As it turned out, the only places we had enough probable cause for a search warrant were the warehouse, the semitruck, all the vehicles inside the warehouse, and the van we had stopped. Unfortunately, per the judge, we couldn't obtain search warrants for Edgar Robles and the Sousa go-cart racetrack business. Unless Edgar decided to flee, we would have to wait for things to settle down and begin a new case on him.

Detectives Carroll, Sears, and I searched the van and took inventory of the evidence. There was a total of 325 kilos of cocaine with a total street value well over $32 million. We secured the cocaine and the van and transported them to the Torrance Police Department.

While we were busy with the van, Sergeant Dalton contacted a property manager for all the warehouses in the industrial area. The property manager was very cooperative and gave Sergeant Dalton and his crime impact team access to another warehouse that was identical to the one where we were going to serve a warrant.

He and his team used the warehouse to practice their search warrant entry. This would be essential to the success of serving a search warrant on such a large place. The property manager gave Sergeant Dalton the keys to the warehouse where the two Latinos and the semitruck were, and Sergeant Dalton drew up a game plan for his team's entry. Detectives Carroll, Mack, and I were also going to enter the warehouse with the crime impact team, while the rest of the narcotic team covered the outside perimeter. We planned to enter quickly through the rear door. While we weren't concerned about evidence being destroyed, we were worried the suspects inside might be armed or have time to arm themselves.

We unlocked the rear door and entered while Sergeant Dalton and his team circled the warehouse counterclockwise. Detectives Carroll, Mack, and I positioned ourselves at the rear door of the semitruck. Upon entering the warehouse, Sergeant Dalton identified us as police officers to anyone inside, ordering them to show themselves. Suddenly, both Latinos came running out from the bed of the semitruck, where they may have been sleeping.

Both Latinos ran toward the back door of the warehouse. What they didn't see were Detectives Prescott and Vaughn, who were hidden behind a pillar adjacent to the semitruck. As the Latinos ran, Prescott and Vaughn tackled both, crushing them to the ground. By the time the Latinos got their bearings, they were handcuffed. The narcotic team then searched the warehouse for other occupants but found none.

Inside the semitruck, the narcotic team found a little over a ton of cocaine. We also discovered four large gas tanks with secret compartments underneath the semitruck. A secret button in the cabin of the semitruck released the secret compartments in the fake gas tanks.

Two of the fake gas tanks contained a total of eight hundred kilos of cocaine. In all, the street value was around $180 million.

*****

Two weeks later, we completed all the follow-up needed for this case for court. We discussed how the last two cases involved the skinny Latino and the pretty Latina who met with drug cartel members, Poncho and Edgar. When both cases culminated, the skinny Latino and the beautiful Latina were nowhere to be found. We believed the pretty Latina was the same Latina our informant said was in charge, and that the skinny Latino was her right-hand man—or 'secretary', as we called him. While we desperately wanted to get enough evidence on these two to arrest them, we knew it was a long shot.

As a gambling man, I wasn't afraid to go after the long shot. Little did I know that luck would provide a payoff just around the corner. I would get another glimpse of our cartel queen.

CHAPTER
28

In between cases, detectives typically followed up on leads from prior cases or from informants. Occasionally, our narcotic detectives attended homeowner and business group meetings to educate them on drug cartels' methods of operation. We explained to these civic groups the history of the Cali and Medellín Drug Cartels, and how President Ronald Reagan and the federal government cracked down on the drug cartels on the East Coast, specifically New York and Florida, causing them to move their operations to Western United States. We also detailed how the cartels were now using local residences and businesses to establish their drug trafficking network.

We specifically educated apartment owners and managers on the usual profile of a clandestine drug cartel member applying as a tenant. A typical profile included traits such as a South American birthplace, claiming to be self-employed in an import-export business, paying rent in cash, and paying rent six months or a year in advance. Most importantly, the applicant wouldn't be the person who actually lived in the apartment.

Apartment owners and managers were told to contact one of our narcotic detectives if they had an applicant or tenant who fit this profile. Occasionally, we would receive a call from someone who attended one of our civic group meetings. We would always follow up on and investigate these leads. In most cases, nothing came from them; but in a few, something big did.

On one such case, Detective Mack received a call from an elderly apartment manager regarding a tenant who fit the applicant profile he had described at one of his meetings. Since the apartment complex in question was only a few blocks from the Torrance Police station, he and I contacted the apartment manager on our way to lunch to review the application of the person she had called about.

We noted the tenant in apartment 215 was a male from Cali, Colombia, who was self-employed and had paid the rent for six months, all in cash. The apartment manager said she hadn't seen the gentleman who rented the apartment since the day he filled out the application, and she had only seen two young female adults coming and going for the last three months. We thanked the apartment manager for calling and obtained a copy of the rental agreement and application the renter had filled out. We told the apartment manager we would contact her if we found anything unusual.

On our way back to our undercover police car, we walked by the underground parking spot for apartment 215 and copied the license plate of a green Toyota Corolla parked there, and then we went to lunch. While at lunch, I called our secretary and asked her to research the applicant's former address in Studio City and find out who the registered owner of the Toyota Corolla was.

By the time we returned from lunch, our secretary had all the information about the tenant in apartment 215. The previous address given by the tenant was a PO box, not an apartment, and the Toyota Corolla was registered to a sixty-five-year-old female with an address in the city of Tarzana. The Tarzana address was also a PO box.

Later that day, Detective Mack and I met with the narcotic team and talked about the occupants in apartment 215. We rarely got a case in our own backyard dealing with large-scale drug dealers. Sergeant Tilly agreed that we should give this case a week or two to identify and surveil the occupants.

The next morning, we set up surveillance on apartment 215. The apartment manager kindly let us surveil from a vacant unit across the way. The narcotic team members took turns watching from the vacant apartment while the rest waited in the neighborhood.

For the next week and a half, the only person we followed from the apartment was a young Latina in her mid-twenties. She was certainly not the sixty-five-year-old registered owner of the Toyota Corolla she was driving. It was a boring period of time, as she only went shopping at the local mall and the grocery store.

*****

Toward the end of the second week, a second female in her late twenties arrived in a red Honda Prelude, which was registered to a male in Diamond Bar, California. While the address for the Honda Prelude actually came back to a house in the city of Diamond Bar, it was obvious that everything we discovered fit the profile of a drug cartel operation.

The new female with the Honda Prelude had two small kids with her. The first day, we followed both females and the children to lunch and shopping. When the female with the kids left, we let them go and concentrated on the female from apartment 215. The next day, the female in the Honda Prelude returned to the apartment. They got into the Toyota Corolla and headed east on the 91 Freeway.

We observed no anti-surveillance driving. We followed the two Latinas to the northbound 57 Freeway into the city of Diamond Bar. They exited the freeway and drove into a middle-class cookie-cutter neighborhood. We followed them straight to a house situated in the middle of the block. Like all the other houses, it was a fairly new two-story family home.

We quickly set up surveillance of the house. They parked in the driveway in front of the closed garage, the passenger unlocked the front door to the house, and both entered. Detective Mack called in the address to our secretary to find out whose name the utilities were under. If the people living at the address were renting, the utilities would most likely be in the renter's name, not the owner.

Detective Sears had the eye on the house, but was on the street and was already getting concerned looks from neighbors. Detective Josh Sinclair, a new member of our team, found a surveillance position off an access road that overlooked the front of the house. Because there was no parking on the access road, we had to park about fifty yards away and walk to the surveillance spot. We also had to climb a tree to get high enough to see over an eight-foot brick wall.

We looked around for a better spot but found none. Parking on the street wouldn't work, as the neighbors might burn us and call the local police, or worse yet, notify the people we were watching. Sergeant Tilly already called the local police and informed them we had a surveillance team in place and gave them his number in case they received calls from residents in the area. The view from the tree was excellent, as we could see the entire front of the house and the garage. The disadvantage was, it was very uncomfortable, so we had to rotate the eye—the person surveilling house—more often than normal.

Detective Sears was on the eye. At 6:00 p.m., a Ford Aerostar van drove into the garage. As the garage opened, he called out that there were small kids' toys in the garage. As the driver got out, Detective Sears described him as a light-skinned Latino with a clean-cut beard in his early thirties. He was wearing a suit and a tie and appeared to be a businessman. As the Latino got out of the car, the same two small children we saw in Torrance came into the garage and hugged him. It looked like he was the father of the kids and probably the husband to the Latina who drove the Honda Prelude.

The clean-cut Latino in the suit closed the garage door. At 8:30 p.m., both Latinas left the house in the Toyota Corolla. We surveilled them back to the Torrance apartment, where they parked their car back in the underground parking spot—space 215. Both females exited the Toyota and walked back to where the Honda Prelude was parked, gave each other a hug, and said goodbye. Because we felt the female in the Prelude was going back to the Diamond Bar address, we let her go. The other Latina returned to her apartment and we decided to call it a night. Prior to leaving, we decided the team would set up surveillance in the morning at the Diamond Bar address.

The following morning, we set up the surveillance. At 9:00 a.m., the clean-cut, bearded Latino, dressed in business attire, drove the Aerostar van out of the garage. We all decided to follow him, except Detective Carroll, who was on the eye in the tree. We followed the Latino for a couple of miles to a Security Pacific Bank in the city of Diamond Bar. We watched him as he knocked on the locked front doors.

An employee inside the bank let him in. When the bank opened at 10:00 a.m., I entered and pretended to be a customer. I saw the Latino from the Aerostar working as a bank teller. It was very unusual for a person who might be involved with the drug cartel to have a legitimate job. When we ran the registration of the Aerostar, it came back to a Rubin Serrato at the Diamond Bar house. Although highly uncommon, there were cases where the drug cartel had either offered money to legitimate, established fellow Colombians here in the United States to help them in their drug operations, or the drug cartel intimidated fellow Colombians into cooperating, fearing that their loved ones in Colombia might be harmed.

We decided to go back to the house in Diamond Bar and continue our surveillance there. Another week passed, and the same activity—or lack of activity—occurred. Every morning, Rubin Serrato left his house in business attire and drove to work. The Latina, who was likely his wife and mother of the two young kids, stayed at home.

During the fourth week of surveilling the Diamond Bar address, we arrived at 7:00 a.m. This time we saw the Aerostar parked in the driveway, not in the garage. At 9:00 a.m. the garage door opened and Rubin Serrato walked out, got in the Aerostar, and drove to work.

Detective Mack was in the tree on the eye of the house. He radioed, "I can see a light-blue Chevy El Camino truck backed up in the garage. It looks like it has a New York license plate." When Rubin Serrato left in the Aerostar, the garage closed and we continued our surveillance on the house.

At 3:00 p.m., the garage door opened. I was in the tree on the eye of the house and saw a new heavyset Latino with curly hair and a heavyset Latina enter the garage and get into the Chevy El Camino. We decided to follow the El Camino with the two new players. We followed them to a small strip mall a few miles away. The heavyset male, the driver, exited the El Camino and made some calls on a pay phone. It appeared that he called a pager and was waiting for a return call. While he waited, he watched people and cars in the parking lot and on the street.

A few minutes later, the phone rang. The Latino picked up the phone, talked briefly, got back into the El Camino, and left the parking lot. We followed them as they entered the I-5 Freeway, heading south. Traffic was moderate, so their speed was about 70 mph. We surveilled the El Camino to the city of Anaheim, where they exited.

Disneyland was in view, and the El Camino drove around it. Our stomachs turned, as we thought they might spend the evening there. The driver went near the entrance, but he just glanced in that direction and continued on. The El Camino then drove to a small U-Haul business about two miles away. They pulled in the lot, both got out, and entered the office. There were very few other patrons there, so we stayed in our cars. Detective Sinclair was on the eye, watching and calling out what he saw.

Fifteen minutes later, Detective Sinclair broadcast, "Our two new players just exited the office. They appear to be with another Latino couple. I don't think they're employees. The Latina is in her late twenties, early thirties—very pretty. The Latino looks the same age, tall, light-skinned, and thin."

I asked, "Where are they? I'd like to get a look at the couple."

Detective Sinclair replied, "All four are in the lot. The pretty new female is pointing at U-Haul trailers as they walk."

I drove by and couldn't believe my eyes. I broadcast, "The pretty new Latina and the thin Latino are the drug cartel boss and her secretary from our other cases!" That got everyone's attention. We knew we had a good case now.

As the four walked the U-Haul lot, it looked like they were picking out a U-Haul trailer to rent. All four walked to a small burger stand adjacent to the lot, ordered food, and sat down at an outdoor table. I positioned myself across the street from the burger stand and took surveillance photographs of them as they ate. I made sure I had several good photographs of the pretty Latina and her skinny Latino friend.

Forty-five minutes later, all four walked back to the U-Haul lot. Three went into the office, while the heavyset Latino backed his El

Camino truck up to a trailer. A short time later, the female passenger of the El Camino, the pretty Latina, and her thin Latino secretary, came out with an employee. The employee and the heavyset Latino hooked the trailer up to the back of the El Camino, and the heavyset Latino and the female passenger got in the El Camino and pulled out of the lot.

Detective Mack wanted to follow the pretty Latina and her secretary, but he also knew someone had to follow the El Camino with the U-Haul trailer. It was highly probable that these new drug cartel members would fill it with cocaine, so Detective Mack said he would stay behind and see where the pretty Latina and her secretary went. The rest of us were instructed to follow the trailer.

Detective Mack saw the pretty Latina and thin Latino get into a tan Nissan sedan. He copied the license plate noting that the thin Latino drove while the pretty Latina sat in the front passenger seat. Due to heavy traffic and being alone, Detective Mack quickly lost sight of the pair. Once again, these two individuals got away from us even though we knew they were probably the ringleaders of a Colombian drug cartel network.

Detective Mack played catch-up once we were back on the I-5 northbound. We surveilled the El Camino and trailer back to the Diamond Bar house. The garage door opened, and they backed the U-Haul trailer into the garage. The heavyset Latino unhooked the El Camino from the trailer and parked it in the garage next to the trailer. The garage door was then closed.

We continued surveilling the Diamond Bar house. At 6:30 p.m., Rubin Serrato came home in the Aerostar, parked in the driveway, and entered his house through the front door. We surveilled the house until 11:00 p.m., when most of the interior lights had been turned off. This case had become very interesting, so we agreed to return to the Diamond Bar house no later than 7:00 a.m.

The next day, we were all on scene by 7:00 a.m. At 9:00 a.m., Rubin Serrato came out of the house and left for work in the Aerostar. A few minutes later, the garage door opened and the heavyset Latino and the same female passenger drove off in the El Camino. We followed them to a nearby Ace Hardware. Detective Mattson followed them into the store. He came back to his car and broadcast, "The heavyset male is buying a couple of sheets of plywood, paint, screws, and a skill saw, along with some other things."

Sergeant Tilly had an eye on the El Camino. He watched a couple of Ace Hardware employees bring out the sheets of plywood and place them in the bed of their car. Our two players followed, carrying the other items they had purchased. The new players then returned to the Diamond Bar house, backed the El Camino into the garage, and closed the door.

For the next three days, we saw no movement at the house, except for Rubin Serrato, who went to work every day. We saw no sign of the heavyset male or his female passenger. On the fourth day, about 1:00 p.m., a stake bed truck approached and parked in front of the house. The truck was full of new furniture—a bed, couch, dresser, nightstand, and other household items.

The heavyset male from the El Camino drove the stake bed. Two other Latinos we had never seen before, were in the back of the truck holding the furniture so it wouldn't fall out. The heavyset male pulled the truck in the driveway and brought the furniture into the house through the front door. When they were finished unloading the truck, they drove away.

Half of our team followed the stake bed truck back to a truck rental yard where they dropped it off. All three men got into a blue Honda Civic and returned to the Diamond Bar house. The license plate to the new blue Honda Civic came back registered to a Latina in Van Nuys, while the address was registered to a PO box. We stayed on the Diamond Bar house until most of the lights went out and called it a night.

The following morning, we once again set up our surveillance at the Diamond Bar house. At 9:00 a.m., Rubin Serrato left for work. We saw no movement all day and were getting tired of nothing happening. We were beginning to think Rubin Serrato was just some guy with relatives visiting from New York, who were helping him remodel and furnish his house. The only thing we were certain of was we were all tired of driving out to Diamond Bar every day.

We were starting to second-guess ourselves, thinking we should have surveilled the pretty Latina and her secretary from the U-Haul business instead. We followed the U-Haul because we thought they would use it to transport cocaine. We knew through intelligence that most of the cocaine coming in from Colombia was going into Mexico, then through Texas, Arizona, and California, because of the heat put on the drug trade back East. We also knew a lot of cocaine coming into California was being transported to the Midwest and East Coast by cars and trucks.

The beginning of the day was like so many other days; boring and uneventful. All of the sudden at 6:00 p.m., the garage opened, and the heavyset male drove the El Camino out. He then backed up to the U-Haul, got out, and hooked the trailer up to the car. He then got into the driver's seat and the heavyset female got into the passenger seat, and they drove away. They headed toward the freeway.

We all surveilled them while Detective Carroll called the surveillance. Since the El Camino was towing a trailer, surveillance was slow and easy. Traffic was extremely heavy too.

Two hours had gone by, and the El Camino was on the 15 Freeway, heading toward Nevada. We had to decide whether to stop them before they entered Nevada and gamble that we would find cocaine in the trailer, or let them go and continue surveilling the Diamond Bar house. If we stopped these two and came up empty, our cover would be blown, and we would lose the Diamond Bar house.

By now it was 9:00 p.m., and everyone was exhausted. The El Camino continued to drive north on the 15 Freeway toward Las Vegas. As they drove through the city of Barstow, they exited the freeway and drove to a Holiday Inn. Both the male and female carried small suitcases with them, and it looked like they were staying the night.

Detective Sears followed the couple into the lobby and stood behind them as they got a room. Sears heard the hotel clerk give them a room on the second floor. We decided to update the ongoing search warrant and serve it for the El Camino, the trailer, the Diamond Bar address, and the apartment in Torrance. Detectives

Mack and Mattson contacted the local police department and drove to their station. Detective Mack completed the search warrant and had it signed by a judge for us to serve.

Barstow was very cold at this time of year, and we were all freezing in our cars waiting for Detectives Mack and Mattson to return. Finally, at 3:00 a.m., we knocked on the door of the Latino couple's room and woke them up. They answered the door and were surprised to see us. Neither one claimed to speak English, but we had several Spanish speaking officers on our team. They denied being involved in the drug trade, and they insisted they were visiting relatives in California and were heading back to New York. Both had identification stating they were from Colombia.

The local police officers with us kept an eye on the couple while we searched the El Camino and the U-Haul trailer. We had keys to both, so getting inside was easy. First, we searched the U-Haul trailer. When we opened the back doors, we only saw the furniture that was delivered the other day. Our stomachs dropped. Maybe the couple was telling the truth. We pulled out the brand-new furniture and searched it. Nothing! Now we were staring at an empty trailer.

Detective Mattson began to cuss and kick things in disappointment. But Sergeant Tilly's brain started spinning. He walked inside the U-Haul trailer, took a look around, proceeded back out, and then walked around the outside. Some of the other detectives gave up on the U-Haul and started searching the El Camino. Sergeant Tilly stared at the side and then the front of the U-Haul, scratching his chin. He then walked back inside the U-Haul, but this time he asked me to follow him. As I did, Sergeant Tilly asked, "You smell it?"

"Smell what?" I asked.

"Fresh paint."

I took a deep breath in through my nose and realized Sergeant Tilly was right. "I do smell it."

Sergeant Tilly pressed on, "Why would someone paint the inside of a U-Haul before a trip? It's going to get scuffed up."

I thought about that one and followed Sergeant Tilly out of the U-Haul. He led me to the side of the trailer. Sergeant Tilly pointed to fresh rivet screws from top to bottom. The rivets were about four feet back from the front of the U-Haul. I followed Sergeant Tilly to the other side of the U-Haul and there were new rivets there too.

Thinking out loud, Sergeant Tilly asked, "Why would they have new rivets on both sides? It doesn't make any sense." He looked at me and said, "There's a secret compartment in this trailer." He listed the evidence; rivets that shouldn't have been there, fresh paint, and new rubber siding on the inside of the trailer. We walked back toward the entrance of the U-Haul trailer and Sergeant Tilly said, "Remember, we saw these guys buy sheets of plywood, screws, and paint?"

We were in the U-Haul now and Sergeant Tilly said, "Let's pull back the plywood in the front." He started pulling back a corner from the top of the trailer while I grabbed hold of the other corner and helped. Detective Mattson saw what we were doing and started to help too. After we tore it down, we stood in disbelief.

Hundreds of kilos of cocaine were hidden in the secret compartment. The drug cartel members rented this U-Haul trailer and managed to build this secret compartment right underneath our noses. Detective Mattson's cussing turned into cheers of joy. This was turning out to be a great case thanks to Sergeant Tilly's discovery.

We then served search warrants at the Diamond Bar and Torrance residences. In the children's bedroom at the Diamond Bar house, we found five kilos of cocaine with the same wrapping that we found in the U-Haul. We interviewed Rubin Serrato and his wife and learned that they were approached by a family friend who asked to use their house for a few days. In return, the friend left the kilos of cocaine and two thousand dollars as payment.

When we searched the young Latina's Torrance apartment, we didn't find cocaine or money, but we did find pay-and-owe sheets. It appeared that the young Latina left in such a hurry that while she took all her clothes, she forgot the pay-and-owe sheets under her nightstand. The list we found used nicknames for all their customers, except one—Roberto Salazar. The list included his address in the city of Riverside.

Documenting a full name and an address for a customer was extremely unusual. The drug organizations prided themselves in their recordkeeping by hiding the details of who they dealt with. This type of disguised record-keeping made it extremely difficult for the police and prosecutors' efforts to locate, identify, and prosecute drug cartel members and their customers. Having the name and address of Roberto Salazar on a pay-and-owe sheet was obviously a mistake on their part, but a gift to us. We now had a possible new case.

The discovery of 350 kilos of cocaine made this U-Haul case very successful. It also showed law enforcement that the drug cartels were getting more sophisticated by hiding cocaine in secret compartments more often. The total street value of the 350 kilos of cocaine we confiscated was around $35 million, but we knew this was just the tip of the iceberg and there was much more to be found.

Although this was a very successful case, we had again, failed to identify the pretty Latina boss and her secretary. Once again, they eluded us. There was no doubt they were big players in the Cali cartel drug organization. We all hoped it would only be a matter of time before we caught them!

CHAPTER
29

A week after the U-Haul case culminated, we decided to take a look at Roberto Salazar. We researched the name and, to my surprise, learned that Salazar was in fact a real person, not a fictitious name.

We discovered that Mr. Salazar was a criminal defense and civil attorney. He had a small practice focusing mostly on minor slip-and-fall cases in civil court, a classic ambulance chaser, yet he lived a lavish lifestyle. He had a million-dollar house on a hill in Riverside and a $120,000 black Mercedes Benz convertible. He wore an expensive Rolex watch and flashy gold jewelry. In short, he lived way beyond his means, which made him very suspicious.

Mr. Salazar became a prime target of our investigation, but we didn't know how he was connected to the Cali drug cartel. We began by surveilling his Riverside house, which prompted us to follow the activity of a few of his associates. Surveilling these new players took us all the way up to Bakersfield and Stockton California—four hundred miles one way.

In Bakersfield, we arrested one of his associates and seized three hundred kilos of cocaine. By the time we got up to Stockton, we had identified even more extensive evidence of drug trafficking. I was responsible for completing the search warrant and getting it to the judge. The warrant ended up being fifty-three pages long and included a total of eight residences and cars to be searched. By the time I was ready to phone the judge, it was 2:00 a.m.

At this hour, I knew I had better present a good and thorough case worth the judge's time and be as brief as possible. Fortunately, I had kept this particular judge, an expert in major drug cartel operations, updated on our case from the beginning. I only needed to cover the activity of the last two days. I faxed him the full search warrant, and he signed and faxed the warrant back to me to serve.

Both the narcotic team and the crime impact team were involved in executing the warrant. In Bakersfield, the crime impact team arrested two more suspects and confiscated another three hundred kilos of cocaine. In Stockton, our narcotic team seized one thousand kilos of cocaine from a minivan and a motel room where the minivan was parked. We took two more people into custody.

Detective Mack and I took possession of the one thousand kilos of cocaine and placed them in the back seat of our undercover cars. At 4:30 a.m. we began the drive back to the Torrance Police Department to book the cocaine into the department's evidence room. By 8:00 a.m., Detective Mack and I were driving 90–100 mph down the Grapevine, which is a mountain range between Bakersfield and Los Angeles County. I was in the lead, followed by Detective Mack. There were so many bundles of cocaine piled in the back seats of our cars that they actually blocked the windows.

As we sped by a California Highway Patrol (CHP) car, I could see the highway patrolman's eyes light up at the sight of two cars flying by him. Both Detective Mack and I were exhausted. The last thing we wanted to deal with was an angry highway patrolman, so we slowed down to get the stop over with. I pulled over to the side of the road, and Detective Mack did the same twenty yards behind me.

The CHP officer sped up to us with his lights flashing and siren on. He parked between us, which was not a good move if we were, in fact, bad guys. This officer only had one thing on his mind and that was to scratch out two very expensive tickets. He approached my car on the passenger side with his ticket book in hand and a grin from ear to ear. It amazed me that he had his ticket book in hand instead of a weapon, but to each his own.

He looked in my back seat and saw the kilos of cocaine, but nothing registered except writing me a ticket. I started laughing to myself now, pissing this guy off. The officer's grin turned into a "fuck-you" look as he slammed his ticket book on the hood of my car and yelled for my license and registration.

I identified myself as a police officer and attempted to explain that we had just culminated a major narcotic case and were driving back to the city of Torrance. But this guy was so focused on issuing me a ticket that he didn't even notice that I was in a police car myself, with half a ton of cocaine in the back seat. He asked for my driver's license and registration again, so I showed him that along with my police ID, badge, and the police radio in the car. The CHP officer said, "I don't give a damn who you are. I'm writing you a ticket today."

Now I was getting a little pissed. I gave him a business card with the number of the watch commander on duty back at the Torrance Police Department. I told the officer, "You're embarrassing yourself. You're so concerned about writing traffic tickets when in fact, you should be more concerned about positioning yourself in danger between two cars you just stopped for speeding at nearly 100 mph. You didn't even realize that I've got a half ton of cocaine in the back seat!"

The CHP officer looked in my back seat again and a light finally went off in his head. "Wow, is that really cocaine?"

I looked directly at the officer and said, "Look, I haven't slept in nearly three days. I am tired and I am leaving. Call my watch commander and file a complaint against me, but I am leaving."

I put my car in gear and sped off. Detective Mack followed. The jaw-drop look on the CHP officer's face was priceless, and Detective Mack and I had a good laugh at his expense.

We finally made it back to the Torrance Police station and booked all the kilos of cocaine into the evidence room. It was 10:30 a.m., and we still hadn't served a search warrant at Attorney Robert Salazar's house. We believed the cocaine was picked up from his house in Riverside for delivery to Bakersfield and Stockton. Although exhausted, we realized we had a chance to arrest a criminal defense attorney for drug trafficking, so this made the drive out to Riverside a little easier.

Two hours later, we were at the Riverside house. The rest of the narcotic team was already there. As it turned out, Salazar wasn't home. He must have been tipped off because he wasn't at work either. We searched but didn't find any incriminating evidence in the house or garage initially, so Detective Mack brought his specially-trained canine, Bob, to the location. Bob didn't detect any drugs in the house, but once in the garage, he barked like crazy. Bob was led to the Mercedes where he scratched at the passenger-side back seat.

Detective Carroll and I pulled the back seat off, but we didn't see anything. I looked underneath the driver's-side dashboard and didn't see anything unusual there either. But then I found a button hidden underneath the passenger-side dashboard. When I pressed it, a large compartment underneath the back seat opened. Inside were ten kilos of cocaine with the same color wrapping and markings as the cocaine found at the Bakersfield and Stockton locations. We also discovered two hundred thousand dollars in cash. We were stoked about canine Bob's find!

Our follow-up of this case included the application of asset forfeiture laws. The city of Torrance took possession of Roberto Salazar's house, his Mercedes convertible, and the two hundred thousand dollars in cash. Salazar's house and his Mercedes were sold at an auction, and most of the proceeds from the sale went back to the city. Our narcotic team, over the years, made the city of Torrance millions of dollars. Thanks to the money we kept bringing into the city coffers, the city was very supportive of our efforts to track down drug cartel members.

We later learned that Salazar, of Mexican descent, used his connections with the Cali drug cartel to supply cocaine to Mexican gangs in central California; including Bakersfield and Stockton. Salazar's whereabouts remained unknown, but the case against his associates proceeded to trial. The defense attorneys claimed that their clients had never met or communicated with one another. They also claimed that the cocaine did not belong to them, and they had no knowledge of it. I testified on behalf of the prosecution and presented my link analysis chart, which showed communication between the defendants based on our detailed pay phone call logs via search warrants, and pager calls confiscated from defendants. I also showed the jury photographs I had taken of the defendants placing duffel bags into the minivan where the cocaine was seized.

Finally, we wrapped up the case by sharing our information about these major drug traffickers with the Western States Information Network (WSIN). This network provided a valuable research tool for law enforcement agencies. In the Salazar case, for example, I provided all the arrestees' names, addresses, car descriptions, pager numbers, stash pad locations, etc. My name was also available to any law enforcement agency that might request further information on data found in the WISN.

Cocaine found in closet of stash house.

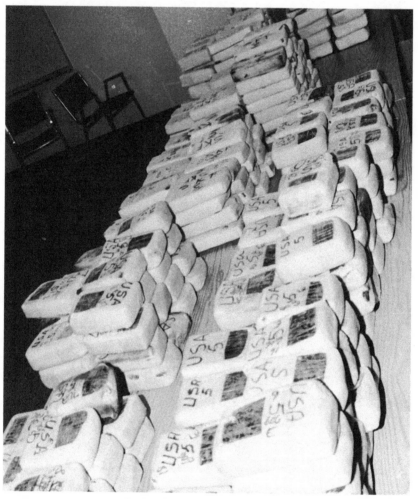

812 pounds of cocaine seized.

Cocaine found in closet of stash house.

Money seizure.

Money seizure.

Money seizure.

News conference on cocaine seizure.

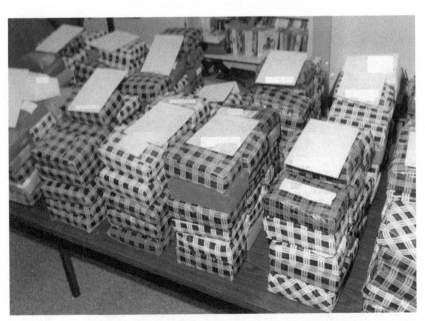

Cocaine wrapped in multi-colored packages.

Semi truck cab seized.

Semi truck with secret compartment holding cocaine.

Money hidden in fake gas tank.

Team with cocaine seized.

Team with cocaine seized.

Team in front of more than one million dollars seized.

Eight tons of marijuana wrapped to look like insulation rolls.

CHAPTER
30

Several weeks passed. One hot summer day around 6:00 p.m., the entire narcotic team was sitting in the office, working up cases and just BS-ing. Detective Mattson received a page from one of his Colombian drug cartel informants that he nicknamed Wally.

Wally immediately answered Detective Mattson's call. He was very vocal and agitated as he spoke. We could hear Detective Mattson repeatedly tell Wally to slow down, as his English was broken, and he couldn't understand him. Wally was a well-connected Colombian drug cartel member who moved a lot of money and cocaine for the drug cartels.

Wally told Detective Mattson that he had received a call from the bosses in Colombia and was directed to meet a couple of guys. Wally was speaking fast. "I'm worried—I know the guys are probably a Colombian hit squad. The bosses from Colombia sent them to take some sort of action—to make a statement. They flew in this morning and are probably going to do their thing and fly back to Colombia tonight," he said.

Detective Mattson asked, "Why do you think the Colombian hit squad was sent here?"

"I'm not sure—but I do know my customer is behind in his payments from previous cocaine sales. I'm afraid they're going to kill the customer or kill us both."

"When and where are you supposed to have this meeting?"

"I'm supposed to meet them in about 15 minutes at Denny's—the one on Pacific Coast Highway, just off the 110 Freeway in the city of Wilmington."

Detective Mattson almost hit the ceiling, yelling at Wally, "Why the fuck did you wait until the last minute to tell me?"

Wally replied, "I was scared."

"Where are you now?"

"I'm down the street from Denny's—at a pay phone."

Detective Mattson tried to regain his composure and asked, "And what do you want from me?"

"I thought you and your team could protect me and cover the meeting—in case I need help."

Detective Mattson warned, "Do not meet these guys under any circumstances."

"I can't do that. If I don't meet them, my family will be killed."

"Do not meet these guys!"

"That's impossible—I only have ten minutes to get there." He then told Detective Mattson he was sorry and hung up the phone.

Detective Mattson looked at Sergeant Tilly and the rest of us and asked, "Well? What should we do?" After a short discussion and because time was ticking, we decided to drive to Denny's and surveil the parking lot and restaurant to see if Wally was in danger. We got into our undercover cars and raced there.

On the way, Sergeant Tilly called Sergeant Dalton and told him what we potentially had and where we were headed. He asked if the crime impact team could help. Sergeant Tilly knew Sergeant Dalton and his team were more physically and mentally equipped to handle potential street warfare than his team. Sergeant Dalton replied, "We're about forty minutes away in South Los Angeles, but we'll head your way."

Our narcotics team arrived at Denny's, and we set up surveillance of the restaurant and parking lot. Detective Mattson located Wally's red Toyota pickup truck with a white shell behind Denny's. There were about twenty other cars in the parking lot as well. We had no idea if our informant, Wally, was having a meeting with the

Columbians inside Denny's. The only way to find out was to go in, act like customers, and see for ourselves.

Detective Mattson said, "I don't want to go into Denny's because it might startle Wally." Instead, he sent Detective Carroll in, as Wally had never seen him before, but Detective Carroll had seen Wally on prior surveillances. Detective Carroll drove to the Denny's, parked his undercover car, and walked in. I drove into a car dealership just west of the Denny's parking lot and got a good eye of the entire area. Detective Mack positioned himself just north in an apartment building parking lot across the street from Denny's. Everyone else positioned themselves on Pacific Coast Highway, so they could surveil anyone who needed to be followed.

Detective Carroll walked into Denny's, headed directly to the front counter, and sat down. The waitress handed him a menu and he ordered an ice tea, cheeseburger, and fries. While he was waiting, Detective Carroll scanned the restaurant and saw Wally sitting in a booth with three other Latinos. It appeared that all four Latinos, including our informant, were deep in conversation.

Detective Carroll got up and went into the bathroom. Once inside, he made sure he was alone and quickly used his portable police radio to broadcast what he had seen. He described the three new Latinos, including what they were wearing. Carroll tucked his radio in his front waistband, covered it with his shirt, and returned to his seat at the counter.

Ten minutes later, the waitress returned with Carroll's food. Carroll had only taken three bites when Wally and the three other Latinos stood up from the table and walked toward the doors to exit the restaurant. Carroll pulled out his portable radio, hunched over so no one could see him, and whispered, "Our players are leaving." He then tucked his radio back in his waistband and finished eating.

Sergeant Tilly paged Detective Carroll and entered "10-4", so Carroll knew we had copied his broadcast. Detective Carroll watched the three new Latinos and Wally exit the restaurant. All four walked to the parking lot behind the restaurant, out of his view. Carroll didn't want to exit and get in his car in front of them because it would be too obvious. Drug cartel members are very aware of their surroundings, and he didn't want to tip them off.

I had the eye on Wally and the three Latinos. Detective Mack was across the street with an eye as well. I told Mack to take over calling the surveillance as I was snapping photos of them. Detective Mack broadcast, "The four Latinos, including our informant, just walked over to a newer green four-door Toyota Corolla. They're standing near the trunk and talking."

The green Corolla had no license plates, only paper plates. Detective Mack said, "Our informant, Wally, is walking to his Toyota pickup. It's four stalls away from our new players green Toyota Corolla." During all this, I continued taking surveillance photos. Detective Mack then said, "The tallest of the three Latinos, who's wearing a blue button-down dress shirt, pulled a key from his pocket. He's looking around the parking lot. Now he's opening the trunk to the green Corolla."

The tall Latino with the blue shirt pulled out what looked like two Uzi submachine guns and handed one to each of the other Latinos. He then pulled out a Colt semiautomatic handgun and put it in his waistband. This immediately upped the playing field. We were outpowered by the Uzis.

At the time, our undercover officers carried Colt .45 handguns with a capacity to hold thirteen rounds in the magazine and one in the chamber, giving us fourteen rounds of firepower. Most of our team carried sawed-off pistol grip shotguns with 00 buck ammo. We used those weapons for up close encounters with great accuracy, as the blast from these guns covered a wide range, up close. However, we were no match for the Uzis, which could fire six hundred rounds a minute.

At this point, we were screwed. We couldn't take immediate action and rush in there, as two of the guys were holding Uzis. But we also knew we couldn't just let them go. We had to take some sort of action. As we discussed our options over the radio with one another, our informant, Wally, started his Toyota truck. The Latino in the blue button-down shirt with the Colt in his waistband, jogged over to Wally's truck, jumped into the passenger seat, and Wally drove out of the parking lot. The two remaining hit squad guys holding Uzis quickly got into their green Toyota Corolla and followed Wally eastbound on Pacific Coast Highway.

Sergeant Tilly broadcast, "Let's go with them. I'm on the phone with LAPD to see if we can get some backup." Detective Mattson, who was east of Denny's, called the surveillance of Wally's truck as well as the two Colombian hit men in the Toyota Corolla. He was in front and called the mobile surveillance from his rearview mirror.

Sergeant Tilly came on the radio and announced, "We're on our own. LAPD cannot help us."

Sergeant Dalton said, "My team's listening. We're twenty minutes out."

While we surveilled both Wally's truck and the green Toyota Corolla eastbound Pacific Coast Highway, we quickly weighed our options for taking the three Colombian hit men down and decided on one. We had to take them by surprise—take them down fast, in unison, and use our manpower advantage—and take them while they're still seated in their car. This would restrict their movement and give us somewhat of an edge.

Detective Mattson, who was still out in front calling the surveillance, broadcast, "The Toyota truck with our informant and the Latino in the blue dress shirt turned left on Fries Street."

Then Detective Carroll called out, "The Corolla with the two Latinos with Uzis turned right on Pacific Avenue." Now we were in a world of hurt. The two suspect vehicles had gone in opposite directions and unknowingly split our team up.

The sun had set, it was dark, and this part of town had few streetlights for visibility. Sergeant Dalton came on air and said he was still fifteen minutes out. He and the cast of characters on his crime impact team, a team that never backed away from trouble, were probably driving like maniacs to get to our location.

Detectives Carroll and Sinclair made the right turn with the Corolla, while Detectives Mack and I took two separate streets and paralleled.

Detective Mattson broadcast, "Our Latino with the blue button-down shirt in our informant's Toyota pickup truck just got out of the truck with the informant. They're entering an auto body shop on the corner of Fries Street and Pacific Coast Highway."

Because Detective Mattson and Detective Carroll were transmitting at the same time, everything was garbled and no one was able to hear what the others were doing. This was what we called a clusterfuck! Our current situation was extremely dangerous—and now our team was divided and was surveilling three heavily armed men that we thought were a Colombian drug cartel hit squad. The potential for a disastrous outcome was real.

Detectives Carroll, Sinclair, Mack, and I continued to surveil the two hit men in the green Toyota Corolla as it drove into a section of Wilmington that was very deserted at this time of night. Each block contained large half-acre to one-acre industrial lots with fifteen-foot aluminum fences dividing the properties. We saw no people on the streets or in the industrial lots. Basically, it was a ghost town, something from a horror movie where only bad things happen.

There were no streetlights, no traffic lights, and no street signs to let everyone else know where we were. It was almost impossible to surveil the Corolla with the two Latinos in it without being detected. Only one of us would go down a street with the Corolla, and we did it with our lights off and far, far back. The rest of us would parallel and get a partial view of the Corolla at unmarked intersections.

As we followed the Corolla, Detective Mattson broadcast, "Wally just exited the auto body shop and left in his Toyota truck."

Detectives Carroll, Sinclair, Mack, and I had no idea what Detective Mattson was talking about, as we couldn't hear his previous broadcast. The last thing we had heard from Detective Mattson was that our informant and the Latino with the blue shirt had pulled over to a curb at Pacific Coast Highway and Fries Street. We then heard him say, "Let him go," meaning his informant, as they were focused on the Latino with the blue dress shirt.

Due to the darkness and distance we were surveilling from, we lost the Corolla. Detective Carroll let Detective Mattson know to be on the lookout for it.

Sergeant Tilly instructed Carroll, Sinclair, Mack and I. "Come back to our location at the body shop."

Detective Mattson, who was on the eye of the body shop, broadcast, "I think the Corolla just arrived at the body shop. It went down the back alley at the rear of the business."

Sergeant Tilly was on the street, east of where the Corolla would have to exit. Detectives Carroll, Sinclair, Mack, and I made it back to the body shop just as Sergeant Tilly called, "The green Toyota Corolla is exiting the alley and is headed eastbound on Pacific Coast Highway. There are four people in the car now. The new fourth player is in the front passenger seat. The Latino in the blue shirt who was in the auto body shop and seems to be the leader, is sitting right behind the front passenger."

No one said anything, but we were all thinking the same thing—the passenger in the front seat is a dead man.

Sergeant Tilly said, "The green Toyota Corolla made a right turn on Pacific Avenue and is heading south."

We scrambled to catch up but by the time we arrived, the Corolla had driven back into a deserted area of the industrial lots. Detective Mack had the call from far back, and I was right behind him. The Corolla had its lights on, but its interior was pitch-dark. We knew that Sergeant Dalton and the crime impact team were in the area but were keeping off the radio frequency, so they didn't override Detective Mack's transmission.

The Corolla was driving very slowly, maybe 10 mph. Suddenly, Detective Mack and I heard a loud gunshot and saw a bright flash from within the interior of the Corolla.

Mack broadcast what had happened. "They just opened the front passenger door and kicked a body out of the moving Corolla."

He accelerated and got right up on the Corolla. Because Mack and I still didn't have our lights on, the three Colombian hit men didn't notice us. We had to swerve around the body they had dumped on the street.

When we reached the next intersection, Mack told me to take the call broadcasting the surveillance. We had no idea where the rest of the narcotic team or the crime impact team were because everyone stayed off the radio frequency. It was game time. Mack and I knew our guys were close, and we knew we had to take these dangerous criminals down. There were no innocent citizens in the area, and thus, no innocent collateral lives could be taken, except ours.

The Corolla reached the next block and veered to make a right turn. I broadcast its movements as Detective Mack concentrated on his next move. When the Toyota Corolla turned right, the two guys in the back seat turned around and looked right at Detective Mack. As they did, Detective Mack rammed his car into the Corolla's right rear bumper, spinning it around. The Corolla's front end now faced the curb, and the car was stalled.

Detective Mack's car faced the rear and part of the passenger side of the Corolla. I faced the entire passenger side. Detective Mack and I jumped out of our cars with our Colt .45s in hand and took cover behind our cars. Suddenly, both of us were taking on multiple rounds from the Uzi submachine guns. The passenger windows of the Corolla blew out. Mack and I were in a world of hurt and we hunkered down behind our engine blocks and took on volleys of bullet rounds, so we were unable to return fire.

All three Colombian hit squad guys focused on me and Mack, continuing to riddle our cars with bullets. At that moment, the cavalry came to the rescue! As Mack and I huddled, Sergeant Dalton and Detectives Vaughn and Prescott came flying up in their cars from the opposite side of the Corolla. All three, with their pistol-grip shotguns loaded with 00 buck, opened fire on the hit men in the Corolla. All three emptied their shotguns, dropped them, and pulled their Colt .45s and continued the firefight until the Colombian goons stopped firing.

Silence and smoke filled the air. Detective Mack looked up over his car hood and made eye contact with Detective Vaughn and said, "What took you guys so long?"

Detective Vaughn just grinned as he and Sergeant Dalton approached the Corolla and checked the three Colombians vital signs. All three were dead.

Detectives Sears and Sinclair returned to the body that was kicked out of the Corolla earlier. The guy was still alive with a gunshot wound to his stomach. He was the owner of the auto body shop and couldn't have been happier to see us.

CHAPTER
31

A year went by. Like the rest of the country, Southern California continued to see an influx of cocaine into its cities. The Torrance Police Department continued to make large cocaine and money seizures throughout the state. During our arrests of Colombian drug cartel members, we would occasionally get a few to talk about their narcotic organizations.

We discovered a common theme among all who talked with us. Apparently, the main person in charge was a pretty Colombian woman with long brown hair and dark eyes. According to the drug cartel members, she was one of the top officials and was responsible for most of the cocaine coming into the Western United States. One drug cartel member said she went by the name Isabella.

He described her as a no-nonsense person who ran her cocaine enterprise through a close-knit group of friends that she trusted. Rumor had it that those who stole from her or betrayed her would suddenly disappear, never to be heard from again. He also said that very few drug cartel members, no matter what their role was within Isabella's organization, would even think about betraying her because everyone feared her.

Those who talked said that Isabella had a right-hand man named Santiago, who oversaw the shipments of cocaine when they entered the United States and to their destinations throughout America. Santiago also oversaw the money from cocaine sales and made sure it was funneled back to the bosses in Colombia. He was described as a thin Latino in his late twenties or early thirties with wavy dark-black hair.

Based on the descriptions from all our recent informants, we determined that the pretty Latina and the thin Latino were Isabella and Santiago. The same two we had previously seen on a few of our cases. It made sense to us now, why these two were so elusive, and why we had only seen them for short periods of time. They were the bosses, and they were involved in the organizational part, not the everyday, hands-on part of the business.

The cocaine and the money laundering continued to thrive in our communities, but we never once saw Isabella or Santiago. By all accounts, they were still in charge but had obviously insulated themselves with layers of protection from law enforcement. When we arrested drug cartel members, we gained not only intelligence from our interviews but also information from the paperwork we collected from their stash houses and personal residences.

On several occasions, we seized large semitrailers with hidden compartments used to store cocaine. The truck manifests documented that the trips originated in a small Texas town called Del Rio. Several of the manifests indicated they had maintenance completed at the same Del Rio truck shop. Each truck also had secret compartments where we found hundreds of kilos of cocaine. We logged these details into the National Information Network (NIN), a database that law enforcement shared.

It was the late 1980s, and most of the cocaine brought into the United States was coming from Colombia through Mexico. Because Del Rio, Texas, bordered Mexico, we felt that the cocaine was being brought in from Mexico through Del Rio.

Shortly after we entered information into the NIN database, Lieutenant Pagh received a call from Steve Ritter, a drug enforcement agent from San Antonio. He explained that he was working a multi-agency task force out of Del Rio and that their task force included a federal prosecutor, the DEA, US Customs, and the local Del Rio law enforcement agency. Agent Ritter explained that he had read about our cases in the NIN database, including details on the trucks we had seized. He believed our cases were directly related to a case they were working on in Del Rio.

Agent Ritter said, "We have arrested several Mexican nationals who were driving trucks with secret compartments containing large amounts of cocaine. We believe the truck maintenance shop in Del Rio is involved. We have information about the Cali drug cartel flying large amounts of cocaine into small Mexican airstrips on the Mexico side. The Mexicans are using trucks to transport the cocaine across the border and delivering it to the truck maintenance shop in Del Rio."

Ritter's task force believed the cocaine that made it through the Del Rio border crossing was hidden at the truck maintenance shop until it was ready to be moved. The truck maintenance shop built the secret compartments for the trucks before transporting the cocaine and marijuana throughout the United States. Once the trucks made it to their destinations in the Western United States, the Colombian drug cartels took back control of the cocaine and distributed it throughout the United States.

Agent Ritter asked Lieutenant Pagh if he and a customs agent could come up to the city of Torrance and review our casebooks to see if their cases were related to ours. Ritter said, "I believe that most of the cocaine coming into the western part of the United States is coming up through Del Rio. Obviously, our goal is to shut down the flow of cocaine coming through the Del Rio border, but also to arrest and indict the family-run truck shop business in Del Rio." Lieutenant Pagh invited Agent Ritter to come and review our casebooks, giving him my name and pager number.

A month later, I received a phone number on my pager I didn't recognize. When I called, it was Agent Steve Ritter from the DEA.

Ritter said, "Me and my partner are in Torrance. Can I come over to the station and review your casebooks?"

I was taken aback as I knew Agent Ritter had said he would be coming up to Torrance, but he never gave a specific date. I said, "Right now, I'm on a case in the Valley—about sixty miles away. I'll have Lieutenant Pagh contact you and set up a time for you to come by the station. When I get back this afternoon, we can review them together."

"I'll be waiting for Lieutenant Pagh's call," he said.

I contacted Lieutenant Pagh, and he said he would handle Agent Ritter. I said, "I could hardly understand what he was saying! I've never talked to anyone with such a heavy cowboy accent." Lieutenant Pagh laughed and said he too, had a difficult time understanding Agent Ritter when he spoke to him a month ago.

That afternoon, I was back at the Torrance Police station and met Agent Ritter and his partner. When he walked into our office, I couldn't help but notice this towering man wearing a huge black cowboy hat. Agent Ritter was six foot six and 260 pounds but looked lean and fit. In his early days, he played defensive nose tackle in college.

As Lieutenant Pagh introduced us, Agent Ritter reached out his huge hand and nearly broke mine in his grip as he shook it. I noted the big dip of tobacco in his lower lip as he said, "Nice to meet ya'll," in the thickest Texan drawl I had ever heard. Agent Ritter then introduced me to his partner, US Customs Agent Larry Miggy. He, too, was dressed as a cowboy, but I could understand him, and he was nowhere near the size of Agent Ritter.

For the next two hours, I went over our six casebooks with Agents Ritter and Miggy. They learned a lot from our cases, and I learned a lot from theirs. There was no doubt our cases were related. Ritter and Miggy both concurred that the truck maintenance shop in Del Rio was involved, and they would have to build a case against them.

Agent Ritter said, "Building this case is going to be difficult because the family who owns the business has been in Del Rio for decades—Everyone knows them. Also, the truck shop is located just across the border near the Rio Grande, so it will be difficult to surveil."

Lieutenant Pagh was also in the room and suggested we all take a break from the meeting. Once we were alone, he asked me to take Agents Ritter and Miggy out on the town and show them a good time. He handed me two hundred dollars and said, "Don't get in any trouble." I really didn't want to hang out with these guys, as I really needed some time at home with my family, but I did as I was told.

Later that evening, I picked up Agents Ritter and Miggy. They stood out like hookers in a convent as they walked through the hotel lobby. They wore big rimmed cowboy hats, long-sleeved cowboy dress shirts, pressed jeans, huge belt buckles, and cowboy boots.

Agent Ritter had a golf ball–sized dip in his mouth. He threw his car keys at me and said, "You're driving!" And pointed to a red Chevrolet Impala rental car. I wondered, *What the hell did Lieutenant Pagh get me into?* When we got in the car, I asked, "Is there a particular place you guys want to go?"

Ritter, in his Texas slang, said, "Hollywood."

I thought, *Ugh! Hollywood is the last place I want to go.*

We drove to Hollywood and walked around. More people stared at Agents Ritter and Miggy with their cowboy gear than anyone else. They liked to drink, so we hit several bars where both drank whiskey like tap water. I had to refrain and sip on a beer because I was driving. At 9:00 p.m., we were back in the Impala driving. As we passed a billboard with an advertisement for the Tropicana Adult Nightclub, Agent Ritter looked up and pointed. "That's where I want to go," he said.

Again, I was so tired. I thought Hollywood was the last place I wanted to go, until Ritter said he wanted to go to the Tropicana! By now, Ritter and Miggy were feeling no pain and having a great night.

When we walked in the Tropicana, the three bouncers at the door all looked up at Ritter. I could see it in their eyes. They hoped to God this giant cowboy didn't cause any trouble. But Ritter's presence alone fended off trouble, as anyone who wanted to mess with him would have to be nuts.

We sat down at a table and more whiskey was ordered. This place was classic. They had two boxing-like rings. One ring had oil in it; the other had mud. The ring announcer and ref, based on his referee shirt, asked the audience for wrestlers to wrestle two beautiful women with large breasts wearing next to nothing. No one in the packed audience volunteered.

Agent Ritter looked at me and Miggy, downed his whiskey, and said in his thick Texan drawl, "Well, boys, they're calling me!" He stood up and shouted, "Ah'l take 'em on," referring to the women wrestlers. I looked at Agent Miggy as he was laughing so hard, he almost fell off his chair. Then six bouncers positioned themselves around the ring while they looked up at Ritter. Ritter looked at the bouncers and shook his huge finger at them while he said, "No need for reinforcements. I'm a gentleman." The audience laughed hysterically.

The referee told Ritter, "These gentlemen"— referring to the bouncers— "will show you to the dressing room so you can change." Ritter walked back to our table and handed me his watch, wallet, cowboy hat, and belt with his huge silver buckle. He then walked back to the dressing room to change for his wrestling debut. Ritter was escorted by bouncers, one on each side. He put his arms around them, dwarfing both. The audience went crazy!

Fifteen minutes later, the audience again went wild as they saw Ritter come out of the dressing room. The nightclub had shorts they supplied the contestants, but it was obvious they didn't have contestants as big as him. His thighs were like tree stumps sticking out of the tiny shorts. The table next to us had four women. One of them gasped and said, "Look at that body." She nudged Agent Miggy and said, "I'll wrestle him anytime!"

Miggy laughed, "You'll have to ask him yourself!"

The ring announcer told Ritter to enter the ring, which was filled with mud. In the ring, two beautiful woman wrestlers waited. Both were looking up at Ritter with worried looks on their faces. Ritter, instead of bending over and going between the ropes to enter the ring, grabbed the top rope and leaped over into the ring as he yelled at the two wrestlers, "Ah'm all yours!" The audience was loving it.

The referee told Ritter he had to get on his knees. As he did, the bell rang, and the wrestlers jumped on his back, trying to drop him onto the mud floor. The two women, even together, weighed nearly nothing compared to him. Not having any luck in bringing him down, they rubbed mud on his face and tried to pull his shorts off from behind. The table of women next to us stood and yelled, "Take his shorts off! Take his shorts off!" But the women wrestlers had no luck, and the round ended.

The second and final round started, and the two women jumped onto Ritter again. Then from behind, four more beautiful women entered the ring and began wrestling him too. Ritter was laughing so hard he could barely breathe. At one point, he grabbed one of the women, and without realizing it, pulled her top completely off. The audience went nuts. Ritter, hearing the audience's approval, began to rip off all their tops.

By the time the bell rang and the final round ended, Ritter had four tops in his hands. We laughed so hard as Ritter's entire body was covered from head to toe with mud. Ritter leaped out of the ring and walked back to the dressing rooms to shower and get dressed. The audience gave him a standing ovation.

When Ritter reappeared from the dressing room all cleaned up, there were no bouncers around him, instead there were two beautiful, big-breasted women under each arm.

He got to our table, sat down, looked at me and Agent Miggy and said, "How'd I do, boys?"

I laughed and said, "Fantastic!"

The four women next to us asked Ritter if they could get their picture taken with him. He agreed and each woman gave him a big hug. Ritter ordered another whiskey—on the house, as the club was happy he didn't tear the place down. As we were leaving, Ritter received a loud round of applause and catcalls.

We got into the rental car, and both Agent Miggy and I looked at Ritter and couldn't stop laughing. Agent Ritter, with a big dip in his mouth, said, "Let's call it a night." After I dropped them off at their hotel, I drove myself home.

The next morning, I went to work tired with bloodshot eyes. Later in the day, I received a call from Lieutenant Pagh. He was laughing and said he had just gotten off the phone with Agent Ritter. He said Ritter had thanked him and thanked me for showing them a great time. Ritter told Lieutenant Pagh everything that happened the night before, and he asked me if the events at the Tropicana Club did, in fact, happen. I told him, "It definitely did, but you had to be there to believe it. It was a crazy night! I think I deserve hazard pay!"

Lieutenant Pagh laughed and said, "I'll buy you lunch to make up for it."

When Agents Ritter and Miggy left, we all agreed to keep in touch and share information on any cases we thought were related to the truck shop in Del Rio, Texas. Agent Ritter said he'd talk to their informants and see if he could get one of them to tell him who was in charge of the illegal drug distribution organization on their end.

CHAPTER
32

I n late November of 1987, we showed a Colombian drug cartel informant a picture of Isabella's right-hand man, Santiago, taken from a prior surveillance. The informant said he knew the guy in the photograph, but he knew him by the name Mateo, not Santiago. He also told us that Mateo had invited him to Thanksgiving dinner the following week at a restaurant in Van Nuys. When we asked him who else was attending, he said he didn't know. He was positive that Santiago, and the person he knew as Mateo, were one and the same. We told him to contact us when he knew the time and place of the dinner.

Our team was excited about the possibility of finally finding Santiago and to start a case on him. It would be a dream come true if it all panned out. If this person our informant knew was truly Santiago, he might lead us to the queenpin, Isabella! But we didn't get our hopes up, as we had been down this road before, only to be let down. The one thing that was encouraging? Our informant had been very reliable in the past.

We received a call from our informant the day before Thanksgiving. He told us his dinner with Santiago was at 8:00 p.m. at the Cali Restaurant on Van Nuys Boulevard in the city of Van Nuys. Since he was having dinner with several people, one of them being Santiago, our narcotic team wanted to surveil some of the other potential Colombian drug cartel members to their places of residence, away from the restaurant. We called in all our under-cover detectives, including our vice guys, along with detectives who were on loan to the local DEA task force, our intel guy, and even Lieutenant Pagh.

On Thanksgiving morning, I conducted a briefing at the Torrance Police Department with the crime impact team and the other detectives that would be assisting us. I briefed everyone about the potential people who were supposed to be at this dinner. We would have to be ready to improvise and be on our A game. We had enough members to form three six-man teams if needed.

The narcotic and crime impact teams would surveil the top two key players. The one thing we couldn't risk was taking a burn by the suspects we would be following. Because drug cartel members were experts at detecting a surveillance, we didn't want the officers outside of the narcotic and crime impact teams to get involved in surveilling anyone if possible. We only wanted their assistance if needed.

Our narcotic team, minus myself, had already set up surveil-lance at 8:00 a.m. at our informant's apartment in Sherman Oaks. They surveilled him without his knowledge, just in case he met up with anyone we should be aware of. We also wanted to make sure we had the right restaurant location, so we could surveil our infor-mant to the restaurant. The crime impact team, along with the other detectives, would set up at the Cali Restaurant at 6:00 p.m. When the briefing ended, I responded to Sherman Oaks with the narcotic team.

At 7:15 p.m., our informant got into his blue Honda Accord and left his apartment. We surveilled him straight to the Cali Restaurant in Van Nuys and watched as he parked and entered the restaurant. Sergeant Dalton and his crime impact team had the eye on the restaurant, positioning themselves on the upper deck of a parking structure looking straight into the front of the restaurant.

Detective Riggs was on the eye and called, "Our informant was greeted just inside the glass front doors. He's now sitting at a large table with several other people." Detective Mattson then took over the eye because he knew who we were looking for. The rest of the narcotic team positioned themselves around the restaurant parking

CAPT. BRADLEY T. WILSON

lot, making themselves scarce. I had a clear view of the parking lot

lot, making themselves scarce. I had a clear view of the parking lot and was ready to take surveillance photographs if possible.

At 8:15 p.m. two cars pulled into the parking lot. The first was a beige Nissan Sentra with a Latino behind the wheel and no passengers. The second car was a dark blue Ford Aerostar with a Latino driver and a Latina passenger. Detective Mattson was on the eye and calling all movement in the restaurant and the parking lot. He described the Latino getting out of the beige Nissan Sentra—tall and skinny with wavy black hair. As I snapped surveillance photos of the guy, Detective Mattson let us know this was our primary, Santiago.

Mattson asked for a second opinion. Just as I was about to respond, he cut me off and said he thought the female passenger from the Aerostar Van was Isabella. I quickly began taking photographs of her. Detective Mattson asked me and Detective Mack, "Are you guys in a position to confirm the people in the parking lot are Isabella and Santiago?" He knew we had seen Isabella and Santiago up close on several occasions. I replied, "Yes, these two people are definitely Isabella and Santiago." Detective Mack confirmed the same.

Sergeant Tilly advised everyone, "There are only two ways out of this parking lot. Sergeant Dalton, you and your crime impact team will cover the west exit. Take the first car out—either the Sentra or the Aerostar—then surveil it until they land somewhere for the night." Sergeant Tilly then told the narcotic team to cover the east exit and take whatever car left that exit first. He continued, "If both cars take the same exit, I'll make the call on which team will follow each suspect." Both teams acknowledged they understood and positioned themselves accordingly.

Sergeant Tilly divided up the remaining six detectives between the two teams, including Lieutenant Pagh. He wasn't shy and reminded the remaining six to not get involved with the surveillance unless asked. Sergeant Tilly didn't want an inexperienced detective to attempt to surveil a cagey drug cartel member. Everyone acknowledged and called out their location ensuring every direction was covered.

Detective Mattson was on the eye and giving us play-by-play commentary on movement in the restaurant. He said, "There are at least eight people sitting at the table. They're drinking a lot of beer and having a good time." For the next couple of hours, the radio frequency was silent. At 10:45 p.m., Detective Mattson called out, "Everyone at the table just got up. Looks like they're saying their farewells. Some are hugging—others are shaking hands."

The first three to exit the restaurant were Santiago, Isabella, and her driver. Isabella's driver was a Latino with dark skin, in his late thirties with black hair. He wore a multicolored, long-sleeved button-down dress shirt with jeans, a large gold necklace, and a gold watch. As all three walked out, Santiago and Isabella headed toward her Ford Aerostar alone. After a brief conversation, they hugged and Isabella motioned to the driver of the Aerostar to come over to her. When the driver approached Santiago, they shook hands, and all three got into their respective cars.

Meanwhile, the other men from the dinner party got into their cars and left at the same time. Detective Mattson called out, "Santiago is exiting the east exit in his beige Nissan Sentra, and Isabella's Aerostar is exiting the west exit of the parking lot. It's headed westbound on Van Nuys Boulevard." Sergeant Tilly instructed the narcotic team, "You guys follow Santiago. Use radio frequency four, so our surveillances don't overlap."

I had the call on Santiago, who was going eastbound on Van Nuys Boulevard. He wasn't driving out of the ordinary, most likely because he had a few beers and didn't want to get pulled over by the police. He drove directly to the 170 Freeway and entered toward the city of Glendale.

While the narcotic team was surveilling Santiago, Sergeant Dalton and his crime impact team were following Isabella in the Ford Aerostar. Detective Redmond was on the eye and called, "The Aerostar just entered the I-405 northbound. The US 101 is approaching but it looks like it's set up to continue northbound on the I-405." But at the last second, he called a whambo and advised, "The Aerostar just crossed over the raised median onto the transition for the US 101." It was obvious that the driver was deliberately trying to detect if they were being followed.

Unfortunately, the crime impact team had several detectives assisting who weren't used to these types of maneuvers. Some of the detectives took the driver's bait and followed his lead, crossing over the raised median and onto the US 101 transition. Crime impact team members Prescott, Vaughn, Riggs, and Sergeant Dalton were ready for such a move and had positioned themselves far enough back on the I-405, so they could transition normally onto US 101 without being detected. Detective Prescott could hardly believe his eyes when he witnessed the blunder by the two extra detectives. He let the two detectives have it and broadcast, "Stand down! Do not follow the Aerostar! You've probably been burned by our primary and her driver!"

Detective Prescott took over the call of the surveillance as the Aerostar transitioned onto the US 101 east. Right away, he could tell Isabella knew they were being followed. The Aerostar accelerated and entered the fast lane near the center median. Then it erratically cut off three cars and crossed all lanes of traffic, exiting on the next off-ramp.

Sergeant Dalton and Detectives Riggs and Caldwell were in position to exit with them. The rest of the team couldn't take the off-ramp, as they would be detected. Detective Vaughn could see that Isabella was turned around in her seat, looking for people following them. The Aerostar exited the freeway with only Sergeant Dalton and Detectives Riggs and Caldwell following.

At the bottom of the off-ramp, the Aerostar stopped at a red traffic light. The only cars on the off-ramp were the Aerostar van and those driven by Sergeant Dalton and Detectives Caldwell and Riggs. Detective Caldwell confirmed that Isabella was indeed turned around in the front passenger seat, watching the cars behind her.

The light turned green, and the Aerostar proceeded straight to get back on the freeway. There was no way Sergeant Dalton and Detectives Caldwell and Riggs could follow without being detected. Sergeant Dalton made a left turn, then a quick U-turn, and reentered the freeway where they last saw the Aerostar. When he got back onto the US 101, he couldn't locate the Aerostar.

Again, we just missed one of the biggest, if not the biggest, Colombian cartel drug traffickers in the history of Western United States!

*****

Isabella and her male driver, Oscar Chavez, saw they were being followed and were scared to death. After reentering the freeway, they drove a few more miles before getting off. Isabella directed Oscar to drive the van into a residential area with long blocks. The entire time, Isabella was turned around in her seat, watching for any cars behind them. Even though she saw no cars behind them for several blocks, Isabella still wasn't convinced they weren't being followed.

Isabella directed Oscar, "Make a right turn on the next block and slow down, I'm going to jump out. I'll call you in a couple of days. In the meantime, ditch the van." Oscar nodded and made the next right turn and slowed down. Isabella opened the door and jumped out while it was still moving.

Isabella hid behind a large tree for fifteen minutes and watched as the Aerostar's brake lights disappeared out of sight. She took her heels off and ran down the street until she found a small strip mall with several closed businesses, an open 7-Eleven, and a gas station. This part of the San Fernando Valley was poor and populated mostly by Latinos.

Isabella saw a Latina in her fifties filling her gas tank at the Shell gas station next to the 7-Eleven. She approached the woman and asked her in Spanish if she'd do her a favor. The woman replied in Spanish with a Colombian accent, "That depends on the favor."

Isabella picked up on the Colombian accent and asked, "What part of Colombia are you from?"

The woman replied, "I'm from Bogota."

"I'm from Cali. It's nice to talk to a fellow Colombian." Isabella, wasting no time said, "I'll give you five hundred dollars and fill your tank if you drive me to the border in San Diego."

The woman asked, "Right now?"

"Yes, right now."

The woman was streetwise. "Let me see the money."

Isabella reached into her purse and pulled out three hundred dollars. "I'll give you the other two after you take me to the border."

The lady grabbed the cash from her hands and said, "Let's go."

Traffic was light, so the drive to the border only took four hours. They didn't talk much during the drive, which was best for both of them. The woman's name was Diana, and she didn't ask questions until they got close to the border. Diana asked, "Do you want to be dropped off on this side of the border, or do you want me to drive you across?"

"If you drive me across, there's another two hundred in it for you."

Diana asked, "Do you have anything on you that'll get us in trouble if we're stopped?"

"I don't."

"Are you wanted by the police?"

"No."

Diana drove through the border checkpoint and into Mexico. Isabella finally felt safe. She had Diana drive to a restaurant she knew would be open at this time of the night. Isabella pulled out five hundred dollars, gave it to Diana, and thanked her.

"Good luck," Diana said.

Isabella got out and watched as Diana drove back toward the border and out of view.

*****

Santiago transitioned from the 170 Freeway to the 134 Freeway toward the city of Burbank. Detective Sears was on the call and saw no evidence that Santiago had detected anyone following him. Sergeant Tilly got on the radio and said, "The other team took a burn—Isabella detected them. It was a couple of add-on detectives who got too involved—They shouldn't have been following her. Once she realized she was being followed, she managed to lose them."

Sergeant Tilly asked the crime impact team to respond to their location. The rest of the detectives were sent home. Detective

Mack commented, "Bedding Santiago at home tonight is even more important now because we've lost Isabella." The entire team was a little down. For years, we had tried to get Isabella, and now when we finally had her, we let her slip away. The good thing was, Santiago showed no sign that he knew he was being followed.

Detective Sears, still calling the surveillance, said, "Santiago just exited the Riverside Drive off-ramp in the city of Burbank." I took over the call and followed Santiago as he made a left turn at the bottom of the off-ramp. Half the team stopped momentarily for the red traffic light, then proceeded through when cross traffic cleared. Riverside Drive was a two-lane road and traffic was moderate. Santiago drove the speed limit. As he came upon a large apartment complex, he quickly pulled in, barely slowing down as he entered. I called this maneuver out as I continued to drive by.

Detectives Carroll and Mattson turned into the complex behind Santiago. Both detectives were far enough back, so they weren't detected. Detective Mattson called out that he would be on foot and was entering the apartment complex from the front. Ultimately, he wanted to watch Santiago enter an apartment. At the very least, he wanted to see the general area he had entered.

Detective Carroll called out, "Santiago drove to the rear of the complex and used a passkey to enter the underground garage. I'll cover this exit." Sergeant Tilly parked across the street from the apartment complex where he could see the front of the parking lot and building. Detective Mack and I parked and went on foot into the apartment complex.

We saw other people walking around, but we didn't see Santiago. There was a diverse group of people that lived there, so it seemed normal to have us, a few white guys, wandering around. Those of us on foot—Mattson, Mack, and I—hid our portable radios in our waistband under our jackets. We put our pagers on silent mode and turned our radios off.

Mack and I split up and entered different floors of the three-story building. I took the bottom floor, while Mack went to the second where he saw Detective Mattson. Mattson signaled to Mack that he had pinned Santiago's apartment, then stepped away and waited for Mattson to join him. Mattson whispered to Mack, "Santiago's in apartment 221, and he used a key to get in."

Mack went to the bottom floor and used his radio on low volume to let everyone know we had located Santiago's apartment. Mattson, Mack, and I returned to our cars. Detective Mattson informed the team, "I saw Santiago use a key to get into the apartment." It was safe to say he lived there. Even though we had lost Isabella, we were happy with this discovery.

Now came the hard part. We needed to return to Santiago's apartment in the morning to surveil him. Sooner or later, Isabella was going to tell him she was followed. After that, following Santiago would become difficult. Sergeant Tilly contacted Sergeant Dalton, gave him an update, and thanked him and his team. Both teams called it a night and drove home.

CHAPTER
33

The next morning came too early because no one got more than a couple of hours of sleep. Detective Sears was first on scene at Santiago's apartment. He quickly located Santiago's car in the garage. Our narcotic team was flying solo on surveillance until something happened. When it did, we would call on the crime impact team for assistance.

For the next two weeks, we surveilled Santiago, but he did very little. He met no one on his travels throughout the day. He mostly shopped, ate at restaurants, and made several phone calls from pay phones. Each time he used a pay phone, we copied the phone number, the address, and the time Santiago used it. This would be useful at the conclusion of the case, if there was to be one. We surveilled Santiago from 6:00 a.m. until the lights went out in his apartment. After two weeks with no real activity, we were tired, but we knew how important Santiago was. We had to be patient.

*****

Isabella spent the night at a local hotel in Tijuana, Mexico. While she was no longer worried about her safety, she was worried about Santiago. First thing in the morning, she paged him, but he didn't respond. Isabella was set to fly out of Mexico and back to Cali, Colombia, in a few days to meet with the Cali cartel bosses.

On Isabella's third day in Mexico—the day she was flying back—she finally got ahold of Santiago.

Isabella said, "We were being followed when we left the restaurant on Thanksgiving night."

"You're imagining things, Isabella. Don't worry about it."

Isabella insisted, "No, I'm not. Oscar and I both saw people following us, and they were probably following you too."

"I've been watching my back. I haven't seen anyone."

Isabella pleaded with him, "Please Santiago, you've got to get out of there. Get on a plane and meet me in Cali."

"No, I need to meet a friend in a couple of weeks, so I'm staying here."

Isabella knew Santiago was waiting for one of his many girlfriends to fly in. He was a playboy and entertained a lot of women. Isabella had grown up with Santiago and knew him better than anybody. She got emotional and yelled at him, "Santiago! Don't be stupid. You're thinking with your dick and not your head. I know you're waiting for one of your girlfriends. You're making a big mistake."

He replied, "Isabella—I promise I'll be fine. Yes, one of my girlfriends is flying in from New York, but I also need to oversee a large money pickup next week. Once my work is done, I'll fly back to Cali and meet up with you. I'll probably be there in two weeks."

Isabella resigned, "Okay, but please be careful."

*****

The next week, the narcotic team set up surveillance at Santiago's apartment at 9:00 a.m. For the previous two weeks, he never left his apartment earlier than noon. I was the first on scene and discovered Santiago's Nissan Sentra was gone. It figured. Based on the past two weeks, we thought it was safe to change our start time. When I radioed the team to fill them in, I could hear some groans in frustration.

I set up surveillance to the rear of Santiago's complex, covering the underground garage entrance. The rest of the team set up around the front. An hour later, Detective Mack broadcast, "I've located Santiago! He's at Laurel Canyon Boulevard and Riverside Drive having breakfast with a female on the outdoor patio of the Burbank Cozy Café." This was a surprise! As it turned out, Mack was hungry and looking for a quick bite to eat when he stumbled upon him.

Detective Mack immediately set up surveillance on Santiago and his new female companion. She had olive skin, blonde hair, and was very pretty. I dashed over to the café and got close enough to snap several pictures of both while they were sitting on the patio. Thirty minutes later, Santiago and his female friend left in his car and drove to the Burbank Mall. He parked and they entered.

Sergeant Tilly and Detectives Sears and Sinclair set up surveillance on Santiago's car while Detectives Mack, Mattson, Carroll, and I followed Santiago and his girlfriend on foot. For the next three hours, we followed them throughout the mall as they both shopped in many stores for clothes. Then they stopped for drinks and food but met no one else. As a ladies' man, Santiago showed his girlfriend a lot of attention by hugging her and holding her hand throughout the day.

Finally, they returned to his car carrying bags of clothes they had purchased. After every purchase, Detective Mattson checked with the clerk who sold them something to see how Santiago paid. On all occasions, he paid in cash. Santiago drove straight back to his apartment with our team following. He didn't drive erratically or look for anyone following him. He parked in his usual spot. We then set up surveillance of his complex with Detective Sears on the eye of Santiago's car.

At 5:00 p.m., Detective Sears advised that Santiago was mobile in his car and his girlfriend was in the front passenger seat. Detective Sinclair followed then called out, "Santiago is headed onto Riverside Drive northbound and is getting on the 134 Freeway east." I took over the call as Santiago merged onto the 134 Freeway at normal speed. Santiago slowly moved all the way over to the fast lane. Like most drug cartel members, he picked the busiest times to go on the freeways. Traffic was jammed on the 134 Freeway, so we were barely moving.

Detective Mack got in front of Santiago and pulled into the same fast lane, but two cars ahead. He called the surveillance from his rear-view mirror. The rest of us followed from behind. Santiago suddenly moved to the slow lane; the number four lane. Detective Sinclair was one car ahead of Santiago in the slow lane and took over the call. Detective Mack dropped back and moved to the slow lane, as the I-5 interchange was coming up. Detective Sinclair said, "I'm going to commit to the I-5 south because it looks like that's what Santiago is going to do, unless he pulls a last-second whambo."

At the I-5 interchange, Santiago committed to the I-5 south. We were all right behind him. Following someone for hours in stop-and-go traffic is about the worst situation you can imagine. Several hours passed and nothing changed, except traffic got worse. Detective Sears took over the call and pulled in front of Detective Sinclair. Sinclair switched lanes and fell back behind Santiago. Santiago approached the 91 Freeway interchange heading eastbound, with the rest of the team following. He drove for another hour and a half and transitioned to the 15 Freeway south.

At 8:30 p.m., traffic finally eased up, and we were now traveling at about 65 mph. Santiago exited at Elkwood Road and stopped at the red traffic light at the bottom of the off-ramp. When the light turned green, he made a left turn eastbound on Elkwood Road and pulled into the Elkwood Shopping Center at Peak Avenue. He then drove to the east end of the parking lot and parked in front of Denny's. Both he and his girlfriend got out and went inside the restaurant.

At this point, everyone was worn-out. The drive, with all that traffic, was brutal. I grabbed the eye on Santiago's car and the front doors of the Denny's. Detective Mattson said, "I'll give it about fifteen minutes, then I'll go in to see if Santiago's meeting anyone." The rest of the team stayed close by but hid out of view.

Detective Mattson entered Denny's, sat at the counter, and ordered a chickenburger and fries. He had a clear view of Santiago and his girlfriend, who were alone and just ordered. They sat next to the window overlooking the parking lot where Santiago's car was parked. When Detective Mattson finished his food, he returned to his car since Santiago wasn't meeting anyone. Detective Sears was on the eye, as I had to relieve myself and stretch my legs.

At 9:30 p.m., Santiago and his girlfriend exited Denny's and got into Santiago's Nissan Sentra. Santiago drove eastbound on Elkwood Road to Singer Avenue. There he entered an Albertson's parking lot and used a pay phone in front of the store. Sergeant Tilly, on the eye, broadcast, "Is he really making a deal?"

Santiago had obviously paged someone because he made a quick call and hung up. It appeared as if Santiago was putting a drug deal together. A drug cartel member of his stature wasn't usually a hands-on employee—they weren't expendable like a mule. Normally, someone like Santiago insulated himself twice over and had someone else do the dirty work.

We were stunned. It looked like he was calling someone to either make a pick up or drop off product or money. We thought that maybe he had cocaine in his car, and he was passing it on. That would make sense, as he had never once driven erratically when we followed him. He obeyed all traffic laws. We couldn't confirm what he was doing, but we did know he was definitely calling someone and that someone would arrive soon.

Sergeant Tilly set the stage, "If someone takes Santiago's car, Detective Sinclair and I will stay with Santiago. The rest of you surveil the individual who takes Santiago's car, so we can locate the stash house." Everyone acknowledged they understood.

Obviously, this was all speculation—we didn't really know what to expect. As an experienced narcotic team, we constantly thought ahead and reviewed potential scenarios. In this case, everything indicated that Santiago was conducting a drug deal. Only time would tell, and we would be ready.

At 10:10 p.m., a newer white Chevrolet Silverado driven by a lone Latino pulled into the large strip mall we had under surveillance. He parked in the middle of the lot between the street and the front of Albertsons. Santiago and his girlfriend appeared to be waiting for him. The driver walked in Santiago's direction. He was in his early thirties, at least six foot one, a large build, not fat but a thick frame, wavy black hair, and a trimmed beard. He was dressed like a cowboy—long-sleeved, white button-up shirt, jeans, and cowboy boots. When he approached Santiago, he shook his hand.

Santiago introduced the driver to his girlfriend, and the driver shook her hand too. Santiago reached into his pocket and handed him something. The driver then walked to Santiago's Nissan Sentra and got in. Detective Carroll was positioned east on Elkwood Road, where the driver of the Silverado had come from. Detective Mack had the call, "Our new player is in Santiago's Sentra and is mobile going eastbound on Elkwood Road." The excitement all of us felt at this moment was unexplainable. But we all knew it was all for nothing unless we found out where the new player was going. This would be difficult, as there were no other cars on the road except us. It would be a miracle if we didn't get burned by this guy.

Detective Mack broadcast, "Our new player is continuing eastbound. Carroll, do you have the car?"

"Yes."

Mack said, "He's all yours."

Mack made the first right turn he could into a residential neighborhood because he knew this player was watching the move of every car. Detective Carroll drove about 50 yards out front of the new player and continued calling the surveillance from his rearview mirror.

The further east we drove, the more desolate the landscape became, but Detective Carroll was one of the most experienced undercover surveillance cops you could find. As he called the surveillance, he noted and broadcast the names of every side street he passed. And for a good reason because suddenly, the new player turned left onto Galen Lane, out of Detective Carroll's view.

I took over the call and turned left onto Galen Lane. Although the streets were dark, there were some streetlights that let me see Santiago's car ahead. He was about twenty-five yards in front of me, driving very slowly, and I knew he was watching my every move. Detective Mattson was about fifty yards behind me with his headlights out. I could barely see him, so I knew the new player wouldn't be able to see him either. I told Mattson to take the call as I pulled into a driveway of a house on the left.

Sergeant Tilly came on the air and said, "The Thomas Guide shows that the street you are on loops around a park. There's only one entrance and exit."

Detective Mattson, who still had the call, said, "I copy you. We're looping around the park right now. The street name just changed— we're on Wild Horse Lane."

Detective Carroll said, "I just entered the housing track and parked where I'll be able to see the Sentra if it continues to make the loop around the park."

Mattson said, "I'm backing way off."

A few moments later, Detective Carroll broadcast, "I can see the Nissan Sentra's headlights through the trees as it's circling the park."

Detectives Mack, Sears, and I positioned ourselves back on Elkwood Road, covering both directions. Detective Carroll continued to broadcast the Sentra as it continued to loop around the south side of the park. Seconds later, Carroll broadcast that the Sentra was headed back out to Elkwood Road. Detective Sears copied Carroll and said, "The Sentra is back eastbound onto Elkwood Road." This maneuver in a residential area was definitely an attempt to detect a surveillance following him.

Detective Sears, knowing Detective Mack and I were both east, stayed stationary in his car along the curb, blacked out with no headlights on. He had his binoculars and called the new player eastbound, with me and Detective Mack out front. Detective Sears said, "This new guy must feel pretty good when he looks in his rearview mirror. As far as I can tell, he can't see a single car behind him."

Detective Mack said, "It looks like we're in a neighborhood with large half-acre to acre lots and ranch-style homes."

Right away, Detective Sears called out, "I can no longer see the Nissan Sentra."

I was hidden on a side street next to Elkwood Road. As the Sentra passed, I called the surveillance while remaining still with my lights out.

Detective Mack got on the air again and advised, "This is going to be difficult. There aren't any streetlights up here and it's very dark." I pulled out of the side street and followed the Sentra with my lights out. I let everyone know I could barely see the Sentra's taillights. Detective Mack said that there were only a few side streets up his way, and he thought they were all cul-de-sacs.

I called out, "I think the new player just made a left turn, or he's going around a bend in the road because—"

Mack cut my transmission off and said, "No, he just turned on the cul-de-sac I'm on." He followed up and whispered, "No talking." He needed to bury himself—meaning hide.

No one said a word. The next minute seemed like an hour. We had no idea if Mack needed help, or if he was concentrating on seeing what house the new player was going into. We all knew Mack was one of the best narc cops in this business, so we had to trust his request and maintain radio silence.

Finally, Mack came on his portable radio and said he had pinned the house the new player was in. "I'm at the end of a cul-de-sac, hiding in some bushes. Do not come down the street. There are only six ranch-style homes on this street. Our player drove into the garage of the second house on the west side. It's too dark to see a street name, but the corner house is red and has a basketball hoop above the garage."

I drove up Elkwood Road and saw the corner house Mack described. I said, "Mack is on Sudder Street. I'll be west of it on Elkwood. I'll cover the only exit." Detectives Carroll, Sears, and Mattson were all a mile west of my location, waiting for the new player to return to Santiago at Albertsons.

Sergeant Tilly advised, "There's no change on my end. Santiago and his girlfriend are still standing next to the pay phones, waiting. I have reinforcements on the way. Dalton and his team will be here soon."

After twenty minutes, Detective Mack radioed, "It's game time. The garage door is opening and the Nissan Sentra is backing out." He called the Sentra mobile and up to Elkwood Road, going west.

I acknowledged Mack and said, "I have the Sentra westbound through my binoculars."

I was about half a mile west and in a small business parking lot with a clear view of the Sentra coming my way. As it approached, I ducked out of view under my dashboard. I saw the driver and let everyone know it was the same driver with the beard. I called the

Sentra westbound for another minute and handed off the call to Detective Carroll.

Carroll advised, "Let's loosely surveil this guy. He's most likely carrying something he doesn't want to get caught with, so he won't be breaking any traffic laws."

While Carroll was calling the surveillance, he quickly told everyone the game plan, "When the new player hands Santiago the key, we'll let both parties get back into their vehicles. Once they're seated, we'll jam them." Detective Carroll instructed me and Detective Mack to take the new player, and then told everyone else to take Santiago and his girlfriend. He wanted more people on the Sentra because that was where the merchandise would be. Everyone acknowledged they understood.

Detective Carroll asked Detective Mattson, "Are you in position to take the call?"

"Yes, and I have the Sentra in sight."

Detective Mattson pulled in a side street with his headlights off as the Sentra passed him. He quickly turned around and loosely followed the Sentra to the Albertsons's parking lot and handed the call over to Sergeant Tilly.

Sergeant Tilly broadcast, "I'll let everyone know when to converge and take these three down. The Sentra is now pulling into Albertsons's parking lot." He continued to call it, play-by-play, like a baseball announcer.

The Sentra pulled into the parking lot but didn't park. Instead, the new player drove right up to Santiago and his girlfriend, who were still waiting by the pay phones. The new player with the beard got out of the Sentra, handed Santiago his key, and walked back to his Chevrolet Silverado truck. When Santiago and his girlfriend got into their Nissan Sentra, the new player was just opening his truck door to get in when Sergeant Tilly broadcast, "Take them down!"

All you could hear were screeching tires as we all converged on our assigned targets. Detective Mack and I barreled into the parking lot from different directions toward the new player, who had just closed his truck door. I blocked the front of his truck with my car, and Detective Mack blocked the rear. We both came out wearing bulletproof police vests and raid gear, pointed our Colt .45s at the new player and yelled at him to raise his hands.

The guy was stunned and raised his hands immediately. We got him out of the truck and on the ground, and Detective Mack handcuffed and searched him. Then Mack and I looked towards Santiago and his girlfriend, both were out of their car and handcuffed too.

The new player's identification said his name was Arturo Pena. When asked how long he had known that guy, pointing to Santiago, Pena said he had never seen him before. I walked over to my car, pulled out my surveillance camera and showed him some pictures I had taken of him shaking hands with both Santiago and his girlfriend. Pena bowed his head, shook it, and said nothing.

Detective Carroll interviewed both Santiago and his girlfriend, asking who owned the Nissan Sentra they were sitting in. Santiago only said, "I borrowed the car from a friend." When we asked his friend's name and phone number, he said he didn't know it. Santiago's girlfriend was asked the same question and she also denied knowing who owned the car.

Because Santiago and his girlfriend both denied knowing who owned the Nissan Sentra and neither of them knew the owner's name or phone number, the Nissan was impounded. Before the Sentra was towed to the Torrance Police Department, I took inventory of the car. Inside the trunk were three duffel bags stuffed with well over a million dollars. Santiago and his girlfriend denied knowledge of the money, saying the money wasn't theirs. Santiago's identification said his name was Mateo Alvarez. His girlfriend's New Jersey identification said her name was Rebecca Gomez.

When Sergeant Dalton and his crime impact team arrived, we filled them in and told them we needed their assistance to serve search warrants. As the case agent on this case, I first needed to update my ongoing search warrant with the day's events at the local sheriff's station. Then I contacted a superior court judge for his approval and signature, granting us permission to search Arturo Pena's ranch house and truck, as well as Santiago's apartment and car.

Time was critical, so I had to update my warrant quickly. There was a high probability that someone was back at Arturo Pena's ranch house watching the clock with orders that if Pena didn't return in a certain amount of time, all money or illegal narcotics would be destroyed or taken from the house, and the other drug cartel members would flee. This created exigent circumstances for our case. Exigent circumstance laws allow law enforcement to enter homes, as in cases like this, without a search warrant. We could then detain all occupants until a search warrant could be written and signed by a judge.

Sergeant Tilly gathered both teams at the Albertsons' parking lot to discuss the next move. He had Detective Mack respond back to Pena's ranch house and again grab the eye view of the house from the bushes in the cul-de-sac. Sergeant Tilly told Detectives Carroll and Sears, "You two cover Mack—in case he needs backup. I'll stay with Mattson and Sinclair, and our arrestees."

Detectives Mattson and Sinclair were currently processing all the money found in the trunk of the Sentra and getting it ready to transport to the Torrance Police Department.

Sergeant Tilly assigned Sergeant Dalton and his team the task of making entry into Pena's ranch house and detaining everyone in it until my search warrant was signed by a judge. Sergeant Dalton took his team aside and spoke to them privately. They began to put a game plan together about how to enter Pena's ranch house. Sergeant Dalton knew time wasn't on his side, so he had to act quickly. He told Detective Prescott to go scout and recon the area of Arturo Pena's ranch house and make a sketch of it. "We'll use it to figure out the best way to enter," he said.

Detective Prescott drove to the area of Pena's ranch house and parked around the corner. Along with the assistance of Detective Mack, he was able to recon Pena's house and draw up a sketch. Prescott returned to the Albertsons parking lot. Using the sketch, Sergeant Dalton drew up assignments and responsibilities for entry into the house.

Sergeant Dalton and the crime impact team suited up in their raid gear, which included their Colt .45s and new lightweight MP5s with a retractable stock and thirty-round magazines. This weapon was perfect for entries into close, confined areas; like house searches.

After the Colombian hit squad case where we learned the bad guys had bigger and better weapons than us, Lieutenant Pagh purchased MP5s for both teams.

Sergeant Dalton and his team drove to Pena's house and parked around the corner. Sergeant Dalton led his team, along with Detectives Mack, Carroll, and Sears, to the front door and set up to enter. But, just before making an entry through the front door, the automatic garage door started to open. The sound of it opening broke the silence, and the entire team froze.

Sergeant Dalton could see brake lights on a car getting ready to back out. He improvised and redirected his team to the garage before the garage door opened completely. Detective Riggs quickly crawled under the opening garage door and pointed his handgun through the open driver's window, inches from the center of the forehead of the lone driver. In a quiet but stern voice, he told the driver, "Put the car in park and turn off the engine."

The driver complied, and Detective Vaughn reached through the window and pulled him onto the garage floor. Detectives Carroll and Caldwell swiftly stepped in and handcuffed him.

Sergeant Dalton and his team quietly opened the garage's entry door to the house and entered. They were confronted by an older Latino who immediately threw his hands up in surrender. Detectives Mack and Sears handcuffed the Latino and handed him back to the others in the garage. The team crept down a hallway and saw two open bedrooms with sleeping children. They closed those doors and entered the kitchen where they found two more adults; a male and a female.

The team ordered the couple on the floor and took them into custody. The woman, Manuela Pena, Arturo Pena's wife, was immediately concerned about her sleeping children. Sergeant Dalton assured her they were sleeping and fine. She pleaded, "No one else is in the house." We then searched for other people and confirmed no one else was there.

*****

An hour had passed and I had a signed search warrant from a superior court judge, giving us permission to search Arturo Pena's ranch house, truck, and the car in the garage. The warrant also included Santiago's apartment and his Nissan Sentra. I handed Pena, Santiago, and his girlfriend, Rebecca Gomez, a signed copy of the search warrant.

Sergeant Dalton and the crime impact team stood guard over the detainees while the narcotic team, including me, searched the car and house. In the car with the lone driver who had been caught leaving the garage, we discovered a switch underneath the dashboard that opened two compartments in the back seats. There we found a total of twelve kilograms of pure cocaine.

In Manuela Pena's bedroom, Detective Carroll found several thousand dollars in a false compartment in the closet. In the backyard we discovered twenty-five fighting roosters in twenty-five individual small rooster houses. Not only were these traffickers in the drug trade, they also raised roosters to fight. We called the local animal control to remove them. We then searched every rooster house. In several, we discovered false compartments containing a total of over five hundred thousand dollars.

This was a very complex case, as we seized money, cocaine, two cars, a truck, and the ranch house. Through interviews with Manuela Pena, we learned that she was from the area of Michoacán, Mexico, and still had relatives there. We found this information interesting because Michoacán, Mexico, was only a day's drive to the Del Rio border crossing, and Michoacán was well known for their drug cartels.

Searching Pena's house took many hours. When finished, we transported the arrestees to the Torrance Police Department along with the seized money, cocaine, two cars, and truck.

For the next several weeks, Detective Mack and I worked with the district attorney's office to put this case together for prosecution. The rest of the narcotic team started looking into other cases or took a few deserved days off. We didn't know it yet, but our top target was feeling the heat.

CHAPTER
34

Juanita waited behind the glass partition in the visiting room of Harris County Jail. She had been arrested the day before while driving to Houston to deliver Isabella's cash to her safety deposit box. Juanita had been working full-time for Isabella these past several years and playing a small role in the cartel had become routine for her.

When she was pulled over by the patrol cop and later interrogated by detectives at the station, Juanita played dumb. She was merely driving a rental car and didn't know the trunk contained a duffel bag full of cash. She said nothing further, exactly as Isabella had trained her to do.

A Latina in her thirties arrived in the visiting room. Juanita knew right away that the visitor was her lawyer, even though they had never met. The lawyer was sharply dressed and had a no-nonsense demeanor. She took a seat across from Juanita, separated by the partition. They spoke in Spanish in hushed tones. The lawyer took control of the conversation.

"Your old roommate appreciates your loyalty."

Juanita nodded. "When can I get out of here?"

"Soon," replied the lawyer, "They don't have enough evidence to charge you."

Juanita breathed a sigh of relief.

The lawyer continued, "When they release you, you need to lie low. The cops will follow your every move. They'll probably wiretap your phone."

"But how will I make a living?" asked Juanita.

"You're still on the payroll. Your roommate has made sure of that."

A small smile formed on Juanita's lips.

The lawyer concluded, "So you have nothing to worry about as long as you stay out of the picture for a while."

"I will," Juanita assured her.

CHAPTER
35

I sabella was back in Cali and learned of Santiago's fate. She had a rush of mixed emotions. There was sadness at the thought that she might never see her childhood friend again, yet she also harbored anger against him. He had been careless in the way he conducted business. She had tried to warn him.

Santiago's playboy lifestyle was particularly irritating to Isabella because she took great pains to separate her own romantic life from the cartel business. A lot of self-discipline was required to succeed, which often meant sacrificing time with lovers, skipping parties, and postponing even the smallest indulgences; such as a salon treatment or a massage. This sense of priority and dedication was what Santiago lacked. Isabella remembered Diego's words, "It won't be easy."

The funny thing was, Isabella seemed to be the only person not conscious of her own beauty. Most women in her situation would have used such attractiveness to get what they wanted, but it never occurred to Isabella to act that way. She saw herself as a business executive who took her career seriously. Isabella became so good at hiding her private life that only a handful of people knew she was raising a young daughter on her own. For her child's own protection, she never mentioned her daughter's name or where she lived to any associates in the cartel.

Isabella's mixed emotions about Santiago included the feeling of being a bit haunted by his absence. She had lost a key layer of protection in her cartel operations with the arrest of her right-hand man. She wondered, *Is it only a matter of time before I, too, get caught by authorities or am betrayed by an accomplice?* Isabella lost not only Santiago, but also Juanita and the three assassins who went to Los Angeles. In addition, large shipments of cocaine had been recently disappearing in Michoacán after landing on a private airstrip that belonged to the cartel's Mexican connection, Conrado Hernandez. These events left Isabella rattled. She knew she had to correct the situation, and quickly.

CHAPTER
36

The next morning, Isabella was on a commercial flight to Morelia International Airport, Michoacán, Mexico. She arrived early evening and chose a Best Western Hotel in the city. Isabella tried to be careful in Mexico, as she was well aware how corrupt the Mexican government was. She didn't want the Federales to be alerted that a lone Colombian female was in town, as they would surely question her about her business there.

Isabella hired a driver to take her to Hernandez's truck mechanic shop and instructed him to wait for her while she went in. The driver told her he was uncomfortable and asked, "Do you know who owns this place?"

Isabella looked directly in his eyes and said, "You should be more uncomfortable with me than Señor Hernandez."

She got out of the car and entered through the front door. She knew that if Hernandez was there, he'd be upstairs in his office. Isabella walked right in and bypassed two employees at the front desk who yelled, "You're not allowed up there!" She didn't even acknowledge them and walked straight up to Hernandez's office. Conrado Hernandez and his bodyguard were startled when she barged in.

The bodyguard stood up abruptly, but Hernandez waved him back down and told him, "It's ok." Isabella said to Hernandez, "I need to speak with you alone."

Hernandez motioned to the bodyguard to leave the office.

Isabella, in a calm but stern voice, asked Hernandez, "What the hell is happening with our shipments? You're on shaky ground. My bosses are very unhappy."

Hernandez knew that he was on shaky ground and that the Cali Drug Cartel would send hit squads if they knew he was the one stealing the shipments of cocaine and profiting from them. He lied to Isabella, telling her the Federales were pressing him for more money. When he didn't fork over the extra money, the Federales started taking the shipments of cocaine themselves and sold them to Mexican cartels.

Isabella didn't completely believe him. She stared at him with her deep dark-black eyes, trying to figure him out. She knew what he was saying certainly could be true. She knew how corrupt the Federales and the Mexican government were. She also knew the Colombian drug cartels were paying off the Mexicans in order to move their cocaine through their country to the US border.

Isabella said, "Contact the Federales. Negotiate a price and find out how much more money they want for their cooperation."

"I will," he said.

"Get back to me by tomorrow afternoon," she snapped and turned to leave.

Hernandez replied, "Yes, yes—I will."

Isabella's driver looked visibly relieved when she returned and took Isabella back to her hotel where she had lunch. Afterwards, she found some pay phones down the street and called her boss. She explained that Conrado Hernandez told her he would meet with the Federales and report back to her tomorrow. She said, "As long as Hernandez increases his payments to the Federales, things should get back to normal. I'll contact you tomorrow."

Isabella could not have picked a worse time to go to Michoacán. Not only had Conrado Hernandez lied to her about who was responsible for the missing cocaine shipments, but the Federales were about to raid his properties for his lack of payments to them. Shortly after Isabella left, the Federales raided Hernandez's office and arrested him. They discovered a hidden floor in his truck shop, recovering hundreds of kilos of cocaine he had stashed there.

The Federales took Conrado Hernandez to his office where he was tortured and interrogated. They beat him so badly that he was willing to tell them anything they wanted to hear; even if it was a lie. He finally broke down and said, "I'm just a small fish in a pond compared to the Colombian boss who's in town right now."

Hernandez described the Colombian boss as a beautiful woman who smuggled most of the cocaine from Colombia into the Western United States. He said, "Believe me! It will only take one phone call from this Colombian woman to her bosses and the shipments of cocaine will start back up." Hernandez pleaded with the Federales, "You want her, not me!" The Federales took him into custody while they checked out his story.

*****

Isabella awoke the next day to pounding at her hotel door. The next thing she knew, ten Federales crashed through her door and took her into custody. When they got to the police station, she was beaten and interrogated. Isabella thought she was going to die. She was hit hard and so many times, that she saw double and was throwing up blood.

Isabella told the Federales everything about her operation. She told them she was there because her shipments of cocaine and planes were being ripped off somewhere in Michoacan. The Federales offered Isabella a deal—she needed to contact her bosses in Colombia and tell them she had straightened out the problem in Michoacán and to restart the shipments of cocaine. She was told that if she did this, she would be released in time. If she refused, however, she would die a slow death. She took the deal.

Isabella called her bosses while the Federales listened. She assured them, "Yes, yes, everything on this end has been taken care of. You can safely restart the shipments. I'll stay in Michoacán for a while to make sure it's done." By the next week, cocaine was flown into Conrado Hernandez's airstrip. For the first few months, the Federales skimmed a little off the top but processed the shipments as usual through the border crossing in Del Rio, Texas.

When the bosses in Colombia wanted Isabella to return to Colombia for another assignment, the Federales decided to take down two big planes with shipments of cocaine. They then presented the seizures to their local press. They showcased the arrest of the Colombian queenpin, Isabella, who was responsible for smuggling the cocaine into their country. When the Federales took Isabella into custody, they only showed the press about a third of the haul. They kept the rest—several tons—and sold it themselves.

The bosses in Colombia lost contact with Isabella. All they knew was what they read in the Michoacán newspapers about her being arrested for smuggling shipments of cocaine into Michoacán. Although Isabella was held captive by the Federales, she wasn't in jail. She was detained in hotels, apartments, and houses. She was never alone and couldn't escape.

The bosses in Colombia sent word to the Federales that if Isabella wasn't released, there would be hell to pay. The Federales then came up with a scam that they fed to the local newspaper. The paper reported that Isabella escaped from custody as she was being transported to court. The Federales claimed that she escaped by hitting the driver over the head with her handcuffs and fleeing. They created this fiction in hopes that the Colombian cartel bosses would back off. In reality, Isabella was held captive in various locations throughout Mexico for the next year.

CHAPTER

37

During the time Isabella was held captive in Mexico, the Torrance narcotic team continued to make major narcotic and money seizures throughout Southern California. With each arrest we made, we would show our arrestees surveillance photographs of Isabella. Like us, not one arrestee had seen her. All we knew was she had detected our surveillance on Thanksgiving night and fled. We felt she might have returned to Colombia to hide out for a while., but we could only guess.

In the meantime, we issued nationwide warrants for Isabella's arrest for transporting and smuggling large quantities of cocaine into the United States—among other charges. We hoped that some other state or federal law enforcement agency would end up arresting her, so we could extradite her to California for our charges.

One day while out on a surveillance, I received a call from Lieutenant Pagh. He said, "I just got off the phone with Assistant United States Attorney, Albert Tomayo, from San Antonio, Texas. Tomayo said he oversees a multiagency task force being run out of Del Rio, Texas. He mentioned that we had already met two of his task force members, Agents Steve Ritter and Larry Miggy. He wants you to fly to Texas and help with their ongoing cocaine smuggling case. I told him it wouldn't be a problem. You should plan on being there for a couple of weeks."

The following week, I was on a plane to San Antonio, Texas. In another two hours, I would find myself in the small dusty border town of Del Rio, Texas. I was looking forward to seeing that big old Texan DEA Agent Steve Ritter and his partner, Larry Miggy.

When I got off the plane, I saw Agent Ritter, larger than life, towering over everyone. He had on his giant black cowboy hat, cowboy attire and, as usual, a big tobacco dip in his lower lip. The only thing different was this time we were in Texas, and a lot people were dressed like him. As the crowd in front of him dispersed, I noticed he had his hand behind his back. He walked up to me with his big Texan smile, removed his hand from behind his back, plopped a huge white cowboy hat on my head and said, "Tommy, if you take this here cowboy hat off, I'll kick your ass!" I laughed, and needless to say, that cowboy hat stayed on the entire trip.

Agent Ritter and I walked down to baggage claim and I grabbed my luggage—which included several casebooks from Isabella-related drug cases. We then walked out to the parking lot, jumped in his big Chevy truck, and drove to the DEA office in downtown San Antonio.

I was escorted to a large office with a circular table in the middle and was introduced to several other agents and supervisors. Agent Ritter got us some water and said his supervisor wanted to meet me before we left for Del Rio. A few minutes later, a tall, skinny man in his fifties with gray hair walked into the room, extended his hand and introduced himself as Special Agent in Charge, James Scott.

Agent Scott said, "I want to thank you and Lieutenant Pagh for your assistance with this ongoing case. We've been working on this case against the family who owns the truck shop in Del Rio for some time. It's been a real challenge to bring down their illegal drug enterprise. Thanks to Agent Ritter's intelligence information from his trip to you in Los Angeles, we're now able to put a lot of pieces together. I can't update you on our new intelligence information just yet. I'll let the task force in Del Rio do that once you get there." Agent Scott then stood up, shook my hand, and thanked me again before walking out the door.

Agent Ritter looked at me and said, "Let's hit the road—we've got a long drive ahead of us. Customs Agent Larry Miggy should be waiting for us in the parking lot."

As we exited the DEA building, Agent Miggy pulled up in a large silver Chevy Suburban. With a grin he said, "Hop in!" We grabbed my luggage and headed off to Del Rio.

During the drive, Agent Ritter let me know there had been some new developments they wanted to discuss with me. He said, "But we'll wait to cover those when we have everyone together from the task force." Agent Miggy informed me we would stop at a jail facility about halfway to Del Rio to interview an arrestee from one of the semitrucks that came from the truck shop in Del Rio.

We arrived at the detention facility in the small town of Uvalde, Texas. Agent Ritter, as usual, took charge, walking into the facility like he owned it. His attitude matched his six-foot-six, 260-pound frame. He flashed his DEA identification and badge at the 90-pound reception deputy and told her they should be expecting us. She replied, "Just a minute." She checked her computer and then said, "Have a seat. Someone will be right out to help you."

A moment later, a heavyset deputy swung open the steel door to the room we were waiting in and said, "Come on in. We've been expecting you." He identified himself as the Supervisor in Charge, Mike Garrett. He said, "The deputies are putting your man Julio Ortiz into a private room so you can interview him. We've kept him in solitary confinement since he arrived."

Garrett escorted Agents Ritter, Miggy, and I into a large room with a small table and four chairs in the middle. In one chair sat Julio Ortiz, wearing a bright-red jail jumpsuit. He was a five-foot-five, 160-pound Mexican national with greasy black hair. He was surrounded by three large armed guards with their arms crossed. Agent Ritter, twice the size of the guards, approached them and said, "Boys, that'll do. We need some quiet time with the prisoner."

The guards appeared shocked and looked at Supervisor Garrett. Garrett laughed and said, "Come on. Let's give these gentlemen some privacy."

After Garrett and the guards left, Agent Ritter approached Ortiz, who sat in his chair facing the table. He picked up the chair he was sitting in and turned it around, so he was now facing away from the table. He grabbed another chair, positioned it to face Ortiz, and sat down. Ortiz looked frightened.

Agent Ritter said, "Relax. I'm not here to hurt you. I just want some information." He briefly told Ortiz that he knew he was in jail because he was caught leaving the Del Rio truck shop business at 2:00 a.m., driving a semitruck with five hundred pounds of pure cocaine.

Ortiz stared at Agent Ritter as he laid out the facts of his case. Agent Ritter said, "You'll spend the rest of your life in prison if you don't cooperate." Then he paused, letting this information sink in.

After a minute of silence, Ortiz said, "If I talk, my family will be killed."

Agent Ritter replied, "I'm not going to lie to y'all. That's your problem for transporting five hundred kilos of pure cocaine. I can assure you—we'll drop the life in prison hanging over your head if you do one thing—and you won't have to say a word—and no one outside this room will know anything about what took place here."

Ortiz said, "I don't understand."

Agent Ritter pulled his chair in a couple inches closer to Ortiz, so their knees were now touching. He looked right at Ortiz and told him to nod if the truck shop business in Del Rio was making secret compartments in semitrucks and loading them up with cocaine. Ortiz looked at Agent Ritter and nodded, acknowledging.

Agent Ritter slapped Ortiz on the knee and said, "Attaboy!" He stood up and looked at me and Agent Miggy and said, "My work's done here, boys. Let's go." He then yelled out, "Guards!" The same three guards returned.

Agent Ritter looked like he was out of some old movie. We were escorted back to the lobby, said our thanks to the deputy at the front desk, climbed back in Agent Miggy's Suburban, and headed for Del Rio. Agent Ritter crammed a large dip of tobacco in his lower lip and said, "That was fun!"

An hour later, we arrived in Del Rio and checked into our hotel. Del Rio was a border town, dusty and hot. It was mostly Hispanic with a handful of white people. The Rio Grande separated Del Rio, Texas, from the Mexican city of Ciudad Acuña on the other side. The hotel we stayed in was no Marriott but had clean sheets and towels. After we checked in, Agent Ritter said, "Let's go meet some of the boys."

Agents Ritter, Miggy, and I jumped into Agent Miggy's Suburban and they drove me around, showing me the small town of Del Rio. There wasn't much to see and was populated mostly by cowboys and other hardworking types. We drove by the truck shop business where our investigation would be focused; especially after receiving the information from Julio Ortiz. While the building was old, it was large enough to conceal two to three semitrucks inside. The building stood on about three acres with nothing in the back, except the Rio Grande in the distance.

Agent Ritter said, "I'm thirsty. Let's roll." I thought we were going to a local bar, but we pulled up to a large feedstore, parked the Suburban, and got out. The two large doors to the feedstore swung open, and a short middle-aged cowboy with Popeye forearms wearing a black cowboy hat bigger than Agent Ritter's, came out and greeted us.

Agent Ritter introduced me to Sergeant Jimmy Dawson from the local Del Rio Police Department. Sergeant Dawson shook my hand and almost broke it in his grip. Like Agent Ritter, Sergeant Dawson had a large dip of tobacco in his lower lip. Agent Ritter said, "Sergeant Dawson is on the task force you'll be working with down here in Del Rio."

Agent Ritter yelled, "I need a beer!" and the four of us walked into the feedstore.

Sergeant Dawson pointed to the refrigerator and said, "Help yourself, boys."

Agents Ritter, Miggy, and I all grabbed a beer and as we drank, I learned that in addition to being a police officer, Sergeant Dawson owned the feedstore. His wife ran the business, and he helped when he could.

There were bundles of hay piled up to the ceiling. I was in a different world standing there in that old feedstore with a cowboy hat on, talking to these true cowboys. The more beers they had, the harder it was to understand what they said in their Texas drawl.

On the wall, there were pictures of rodeos with rodeo clowns. Agent Ritter pointed to one and said, "Sergeant Dawson, here, is a rodeo clown—does it for a hobby."

I commented, "A dangerous hobby for sure."

It was about 11:00 p.m., and we had to be at the assistant United States attorney's (AUSA) satellite office in town the following morning at eight, so we called it a night and got some sleep.

*****

The next morning, we met at AUSA Albert Tomayo's office at 7:45. The building was no larger than 1,200 square feet and most of it consisted of a main room with a large rectangle table and a whiteboard. Eight people were sitting around the table, talking and drinking coffee. I sat between Agents Ritter and Miggy.

AUSA Tomayo introduced me to everyone, even though I thought they all knew who I was through Agent Ritter. Everyone introduced themselves.

Agent Ritter stood up, walked to the front of the room, and updated the group on his new information and his interview with prisoner Ortiz. He told everyone that Ortiz confirmed that Pena's Del Rio Truck Shop was servicing the semitrucks and inserting secret compartments in them for their cocaine enterprise.

Agent Ritter further explained his most recent intelligence information revealed that the Cali Drug Cartel was allegedly flying large shipments of cocaine into a private landing strip in Michoacán, Mexico. The private airstrip was owned by a Mexican, Conrado Hernandez, who was a known drug smuggler. Hernandez owned about fifty acres of land just outside the city of Morelia, Mexico. Agent Ritter continued, "It's also known that Hernandez owns and operates a truck maintenance shop for semitrucks on his property." He looked at me and asked, "Sound familiar?" I nodded in agreement.

Ritter said, "My contacts from the Mexico side allege that the Cali Drug Cartel pays Hernandez to use his airstrip to smuggle cocaine into Mexico. Apparently, Hernandez then transports the cocaine in trucks and cars along the fourteen-hour trek to the

Mexican town of Ciudad Acuña, which just so happens to be the town right across from us."

Agent Ritter went on to say, "At this point, we don't know for sure how the cocaine is getting smuggled into the United States and into the truck shop in Del Rio. Most likely, by trucks, cars or anything on four wheels with secret compartments—like the ones we seized and the ones the Torrance Police Department seized up in Southern California."

As Agent Ritter spoke, he saw that I was smiling and asked, "Tommy, are you holding back some information we should know?"

I replied, "Yes, but it can wait until you're finished."

Agent Ritter grinned and continued, "I've yet to learn what the connection is between Conrado Hernandez and the Del Rio truck shop. Why are they shipping cocaine to Southern California?" He looked at me and said, "I've got one more thing to show you, but before I do, I want to know—why are you smiling?"

I gave everyone a short version of our cases, seizures, and the background of the beautiful Colombian named Isabella—who was responsible for most of the cocaine flooding into Western United States. I told them of the night we almost had her, but she got away, and detailed our arrest of her right-hand man, the Colombian, Santiago Ramirez, as he picked up over a million dollars from a Mexican by the name Arturo Pena.

When I said Arturo Pena's name, I looked right at Agent Ritter and he smiled. Not everyone picked up on it. I held up my hand as Agent Ritter jumped in to talk and said, "Wait. There's more." I explained, "In this same case, we arrested Arturo Pena's wife at their house after we discovered cocaine in a secret compartment of a car in their garage. We also found a large amount of cash hidden in their house and property."

Ritter said, "So you said you had more." I again held my hand up to quiet him, which was hard to do.

I looked directly at Agent Ritter and said, "Arturo Pena's wife's maiden name is Manuela Hernandez. She told me she was originally from Michoacán, Mexico, and has a brother, Conrado Hernandez, who still lives there." I paused briefly, looked around the room and continued, "On Arturo Pena's booking paperwork, Pena lists Del Rio, Texas, as his place of birth. Until I arrived in Del Rio last night, I never knew the name of the truck shop in Del Rio. I thought 'Truck Shop' was the full name. Last night, Agents Ritter and Miggy gave me a tour of Del Rio and pointed out the truck shop, and I noted the full name of the business was 'Pena's Truck Shop.'"

I continued by explaining that the chain started with the Colombians flying in the shipments of cocaine into Conrado Hernandez's airfield in Michoacán, Mexico. "Hernandez sees to it that the cocaine is transported across the border to Pena's Truck Shop, owned by our arrestee Arturo Pena's family. The semitrucks are serviced at Pena's Truck Shop in Del Rio and sent on to Southern California, where Isabella and her Colombian operation take back control of the cocaine and sell it throughout America."

AUSA Tomayo, while looking directly at me, said, "This is why we need you here. Talking face-to-face is far better than by the phone."

Agent Ritter pulled a newspaper article out of his notebook and handed it to Agent Miggy. Agent Miggy, who spoke fluent Spanish, translated the article out loud in English. The article, printed two days earlier by a local newspaper in Michoacán, Mexico, was about the arrest of a female Colombian drug smuggler, Gloria Sanchez, made by the Federales in Michoacán.

The article stated that as Sanchez was being transported to court, she overpowered the driver by hitting him over the head and escaped. A search was conducted, but she wasn't found. Agent Ritter said, "If this is related to our case, this will slow down or stop the flow of cocaine up through Del Rio. This is why we need to bust Pena's Truck Shop now, while they have product."

Agent Miggy placed the news article on the table. I looked at the picture of the female Colombian smuggler and couldn't believe it! I reached into one of my six casebooks and pulled out several surveillance pictures of Isabella. Agent Miggy looked at my photographs and said, "That's her. That's definitely the same person."

Agent Ritter quickly rounded the table to see for himself. The picture of the female Colombian smuggler in the Michoacán newspaper was absolutely Isabella Herrera. I was speechless. Now I knew why no one had seen her. The story about her in handcuffs and over-powering the driver on the way to court wasn't believable. So where was she? Only time would tell.

AUSA Tomayo laid out his game plan. "I want to start sur-veilling Pena's Truck Shop tomorrow." He asked me to join. AUSA Tomayo then asked Agent Ritter to draw up a diagram on the white-board of how the operation would take place along with correspond-ing assignments. Each agency's operational plans differed. In Texas, it was a different landscape and there were different styles on how to run a surveillance. It was quite obvious that this task force was new, and the team members hadn't worked together for very long or con-ducted many surveillance cases together.

Agent Ritter laid out his operation, which was different from what I would have done. They assigned two men to an undercover surveillance car instead of one like our task force teams in Southern California. But it was their show. I was teamed up with Agent Ritter, so I knew we would be in the thick of it. The plan was to stop every semitruck that left Pena's Truck Shop and search them.

Once Agent Ritter finished outlining his game plan, he looked at me and said, "We don't do much surveillances down here, and I've read your cases and seen your results. Let me know if you'd do anything different."

I said, "I'd probably do a couple of things differently. Do you know how many semitrucks on average get serviced at Pena's Truck Shop daily? And how many go mobile and hit the road?"

Several of the agents said it could be anywhere from ten to thir-ty-five trucks. Some just get gas and move on, but others are in the maintenance garage for service.

I said, "If we were to stop every truck that left Pena's Truck Shop, word would get back quickly, and they'd move any cocaine they had off the property." I then asked, "Of the trucks that were seized that contained cocaine, what time of the day or night did they leave the shop?" I looked in one of my casebooks and pulled out the two manifests from the two trucks we seized that had cocaine hid-den in secret compartments. The manifests indicated they both left

Del Rio after midnight. I further pointed out to the group, "Your arrestee Ortiz, who we interviewed yesterday, was stopped at 2:00 a.m., which means he left Pena's Truck Shop about 1:00 a.m. This shows a pattern."

One of the agents in the room reviewed a manifest from one of his arrests and confirmed that his arrestee had left the shop at 10:30 p.m. I said, "I recommend that we surveil Pena's Truck Shop during the day for intel, and see how many trucks actually leave from inside the maintenance building versus how many trucks just get gas or a minor repair and get back on the road."

I further suggested, "We should notify your highway patrol which trucks left from within the maintenance building throughout the day. Have them inspect those trucks, but do it at checkpoints several hundred miles away. If it were me, I'd pay close attention to those trucks that left the maintenance building after hours." I looked at Agent Ritter and said, "I'd even wait to stop those trucks at a truck inspection point just in case they're clean. Your agents could surveil the trucks to the first inspection stop and thoroughly search for any hidden compartments without the driver's knowledge. All we need is one stop with narcotics in a truck, and we'll have enough for a search warrant. Then Pena's Truck Shop is yours."

Agent Ritter said, "You heard him—that's the plan, boys!"

*****

The next morning, we were on-site at Pena's Truck Shop at ten o'clock. DEA Agent Ritter was my partner, and I had a blast listening to him talk. He was an extremely intelligent forward thinker with a lot of energy. He was like the outspoken leader on the football team. When you were tired and hurt and you felt like quitting, Agent Ritter was the guy who'd say or do something to inspire the team, get them to overcome their pain, and go on to win the game.

Throughout the day, everyone took turns on the eye of Pena's Truck Shop. We planned to monitor and log how many trucks stopped for gas or minor maintenance and continued their routes, versus how many went behind closed doors into the mechanic portion of the shop. We also kept a close watch over any trucks that exited from inside the mechanic area during working hours. The mechanic portion of the shop seemed to be open from 8:00 a.m. to 5:00 p.m.

We surveilled Pena's Truck Shop for the next four days from 6:00 a.m. until 3:00 a.m. At 3:00 a.m., we would have just enough time to go back to our hotels, maybe get a couple of hours of sleep, take a shower, and get back to surveil Pena's Truck Shop by 6:00 a.m. When someone had the eye of the truck shop, everyone else got some shut-eye or at least tried to take a quick nap.

In the first four days of surveillance, there were an average of thirty-five trucks a day that stopped and serviced their trucks, had minor maintenance, filled up gas, and continued their route. Only one truck came out of the mechanic portion of the business and headed toward San Antonio. That truck left at 3:00 p.m. We copied the license plate number, and an undercover unit surveilled the truck to the first truck weigh station, two hours away.

At that truck weigh station, the undercover officers, in conjunction with the Texas Highway Patrol, inspected the truck's manifest and the merchandise the truck carried. This was standard procedure for truck weigh stations, so the search wasn't out of the ordinary. While the search revealed no illegal contraband, agents did discover a hidden compartment in the cabin of the truck. The driver of the truck was not aware our undercover officers had located it.

Upon searching the truck, our DEA undercover guys located a button underneath the dashboard. When they pressed the button, a false wall popped open at the back of the cabin. The space was floor-to-ceiling tall and the same width. The false compartment was empty, so Agent Ritter instructed our undercover DEA agents to put everything back in place and not mention the hidden compartment to the driver. The driver would then think this was just an ordinary inspection stop.

The DEA agents saw to it that the information about the truck with the secret compartment was logged into the nationwide computer system. Now the secret compartment would be checked at every stop this truck made at other truck weigh stations.

By the fifth day of our surveillance, everyone was getting tired, but Agent Ritter kept us motivated and entertained, mostly by laughing at his own jokes. On this day, we monitored twenty-seven trucks that were serviced and then continued their travels. No trucks left from the maintenance shop.

That evening, nothing changed until 11:00 p.m., when an eighteen-wheeler semitruck came out of the shop's maintenance area. I was on the eye and called out two individuals pulling open the two large front doors to the maintenance shop. Out came a bright-red eighteen-wheeler which headed toward San Antonio. A couple of undercover units followed the truck, and we planned to have it searched when it reached a weigh station.

An hour later, a second eighteen-wheeler, blue in color, came out of the shop's maintenance area. This truck headed toward Dallas. Again, two undercover units followed the blue truck to the first weigh station. Both trucks, the red one heading toward San Antonio and the blue one heading toward Dallas, failed to pull over at their first weigh stations.

Both drivers, most likely, thought the weigh stations were lightly staffed at this hour in the morning and probably hoped the Texas Highway Patrol wouldn't notice and pull them over. Neither driver knew they were being surveilled by undercover federal agents. Both undercover agents called the Texas Highway Patrol and advised that the trucks failed to pull into the weigh stations and were possibly carrying illegal narcotics. The Texas Highway Patrol stopped both trucks for failing to pull over at open weigh stations.

The truck drivers were taken out of the trucks and interviewed by one officer while the other highway patrolman, along with the undercover agents, searched the trucks. Secret compartments were discovered in both. The red truck had a secret compartment in the back wall of the cabin which was identical to the one found in the truck from the previous day. A button underneath the dashboard activated the false wall to pop open.

The secret compartment in the red truck contained 750 kilos of pure cocaine with a street value of $75 million. The search of the blue truck revealed two toggle switches under the dashboard which opened two secret compartments underneath the truck. Both compartments looked like gas tanks but instead were loaded with 500 kilos of pure cocaine with a street value of $50 million.

The drivers denied any knowledge of the secret compartments. Both said they were paid to transport their merchandise to Southern California, and they picked up their trucks at Pena's Truck Shop.

Agent Ritter and I returned to his office in Del Rio, so he could write a search warrant for Pena's Truck Shop. In the meantime, the surveillance of Pena's Truck Shop continued. Anyone leaving the shop was stopped, identified, and detained. The two men who opened the large front doors of the maintenance building to let the big 18-wheeler semitrucks out, were also detained.

By 6:00 a.m., Agent Ritter had organized twenty federal and local police officers and served a search warrant on Pena's Truck Shop. The search revealed a twenty-by-twenty-foot false floor inside the maintenance shop building and inside that, agents discovered a little over a ton of pure cocaine, packaged the same as the cocaine recovered earlier from the red and blue trucks. The cocaine found in Pena's Truck Shop was ready to be shipped out through semitrucks, no doubt headed for the Western United States.

Upon my return to California, I briefed the narcotic and crime impact teams on the updated information about the Cali Drug Cartel's distribution organization. I also provided the information and news clippings of Isabella's arrest by the Federales. I added, "The whereabouts of Isabella Herrera remain unknown." While the DEA believed that she was arrested by the Federales in Michoacán, Mexico, they didn't believe the news articles about her escaping. Isabella could be dead, still in custody, or back in Colombia.

Sergeant Tilly said, "Let's make sure we have Isabella's arrest warrants in the nationwide system in case she returns to the United States."

I assured Sergeant Tilly, "I already put Isabella's warrants in the system with my name as the contact." While it took some time, this database would eventually provide a vital connection in uncovering the mystery of Isabella's whereabouts.

CHAPTER
38

B y this time, Nicole and I had two children—Danielle, age seven, and Erik, age four. Our home was in a nice, tree-lined middle-class neighborhood in Southern California. One Sunday morning, a phone call woke us up. Nicole didn't answer, she knew who it was for. It was still dark outside. Groggy and bleary-eyed, I picked up the phone. As expected, it was a call from the station. A new lead had come in on one of our cases, and I had to join the surveillance right away.

I hung up, hurriedly splashed water on my face and got dressed. Nicole sat up and stared at me before saying a word.

"What about our family beach plans today?"

"Sorry, I'll make it up to everyone next Sunday."

Nicole still had a point to make. "You sure about that?"

In all honesty, I couldn't answer yes, so I just rushed around the room to gather the things I needed for work. Nicole pounced on the silence.

"You just got back from having been gone two weeks and now the first chance we get to—"

"I know, but I don't have any control over my schedule. It's the nature of—"

"The job," Nicole said with a sigh. "Yeah, I get it."

"Okay, then."

Nicole looked disappointed. Now it was my turn to sigh. "Look, I know things feel unfair. But as long as I'm working undercover, there's not much I can do. It won't be forever." I then gave her a quick kiss goodbye.

On my way out, I passed Danielle and Erik's rooms, both were sleeping soundly. It pained me to go out that door. This wasn't the way I planned it. I didn't want a repeat of my fatherless childhood for my own kids. I loved my job. It was often exhilarating. But it also wore me out. There had to be some kind of change soon.

CHAPTER
39

When I got back from Texas, things started changing within the Torrance Police Department. The police chief we had for twenty-plus years was about to retire. Rumors spread that the city manager was looking to hire a chief from outside the department. This caused a ripple effect throughout the entire department. Some upper management retired due to an outside chief being hired, and several potential promotions opened.

Most of the members on the narcotic team, including myself, were burned out from working so many long hours. We started positioning ourselves for the upcoming sergeant promotions. In doing so, we all knew we would be reassigned back to uniform patrol in the near future.

CHAPTER
40

The Federales transported Isabella through many seedy Michoacán towns and confined her in so many dilapidated rooms that she lost count. All the rooms were the same—little to no furniture, bare walls, dusty, stained floors, no heat in winter, and no air-conditioning in summer. Her captors took perverse pleasure in treating her like a dog. She was fed occasional meals of moldy tortillas and stale beans. She was left in dirty and threadbare clothes. As time passed, she became thinner and weaker.

Isabella was knocked around almost every day. Her face was swollen, and her body was bruised. But she always fought back, as proven by her broken fingernails and scraped knuckles. She never gave in. She was in survival mode. What spurred her on from one day to the next was the craving for payback. If she ever escaped from this ordeal, she'd make Conrado Hernandez and his family suffer the way she had suffered.

One day, a burly guard stood in front of Isabella. He stared down at her as she sat on the floor against the wall. He unbuckled his belt and unzipped his pants.

CHAPTER
41

Isabella finally escaped from the Federales in Michoacán. It turned out to be simple, actually. She was held in an apartment with two guards. She told the guards that she had stored a lot of money in a safety deposit box in Houston. "If you let me go, I'll bring you back a million dollars." The guards believed her. Isabella fled Mexico to Houston. She picked up some money for herself and then traveled back to Colombia. Her year of hell in captivity finally ended.

Isabella notified her bosses in Colombia of her release. She told them she needed some time off to heal physically and mentally before getting back to business.

CHAPTER
42

O ne morning, I was sitting at my desk when I received a call
from an FBI agent, Michael Saraceno, based in New Jersey.
He said, "I have Isabella Herrera in custody for drug trafficking." I was stunned. Agent Saraceno said, "Isabella put together
a large sale of cocaine with some potential buyers. What she didn't
know was her buyers were undercover FBI agents." Isabella had flown
into New Jersey from Cali, Colombia, and put the final touches on
the sale of six hundred kilos of cocaine with a street value of $60
million. After she finalized the deal with the undercover FBI agents,
the FBI placed her under arrest.

The assistant United States attorney offered Isabella a deal of
five years if she pled guilty. Agent Saraceno said, "The sentence was
only for five years because we never saw any of the cocaine. We only
have Isabella for conspiring to put the deal together. We think she
was hinked up because our agents took a burn." They had to make
an on-the-spot decision to either let her fly back to Cali, Colombia,
and more than likely lose the deal, or arrest her for conspiracy for the
transportation and sale of cocaine. They chose to arrest Isabella.

Agent Saraceno said, "Isabella took the deal. Right now, she's in
a federal prison in New Jersey. When we ran her name in the nationwide database, we noticed you had several warrants out for her arrest
for the transportation and sale of cocaine."

I said, "I have state charges on Isabella and she's looking at twenty-five years to life. She's responsible for most of the cocaine that was coming up through Texas, Arizona, and California. Has she retained an attorney for your case?"

"Yes, she has."

"Can you give me the name of her attorney and the federal prison she's in?"

"Sure. I'll fax over all of our reports and all the information we have on her."

"Thanks—You've made my day!"

I immediately met with Sergeants Tilly and Dalton and Lieutenant Pagh to tell them about Isabella's arrest. That's when Lieutenant Pagh informed me of some upcoming changes. Sergeants Tilly and Dalton were leaving the narcotic and crime impact teams and going back to patrol division, as both were getting promoted. At the Torrance Police Department, when someone was promoted to sergeant or lieutenant, they were reassigned to the patrol division. Lieutenant Pagh added, "Detective Mack and I are also leaving."

I looked at Lieutenant Pagh and Sergeants Tilly and Dalton and said, "What the hell are we going to do with Isabella Herrera? Who's going to work her or at least attempt to turn her into an informant?"

Lieutenant Pagh said, "You'll get the ball rolling and either get her extradited out to the West Coast, or we'll go to New Jersey and interview her there."

Sergeant Tilly said, "We need to get her out here, away from the facility she's currently in, for a couple of reasons. First, we want her to be someplace she's not familiar with, to put her at a disadvantage. Secondly, we don't want the guards who are supervising her to know she's talking to the police."

Sergeant Dalton commented, "That would be counterproductive—the guards could use that against her."

Sergeant Tilly said, "We need to get Isabella in a sterile environment to have the best chance of getting her cooperation."

I said, "Even if we're able to get Isabella's cooperation, it will take time, and you guys are all leaving. More than likely, the entire narcotic and crime impact team members will be back in patrol within the year, either for promotions or because everyone needs a break." I shook my head and said, "The timing couldn't be worse! A new narcotic team can't handle a high-level informant like Isabella."

Lieutenant Pagh looked at me and smiled. I stared back at him and said, "What are you smiling at?" He said, "I'm being transferred to a regional task force, where I'll be in charge of multiple agencies and supervising several narcotic teams."

I replied, "Okay. That's good, but it doesn't change the fact that the narcotic team will be inexperienced. They won't know how to work major organizations like the Cali and Medellín Drug Cartels."

Lieutenant Pagh again smiled and said, "Mack will head up one of the narcotic teams. By the time we get Isabella out here, talk to her, send her back, and then get her transferred out to a federal prison on the West Coast, it'll be at least a year or more. That's if we're even able to turn Isabella into an informant—which is a long shot at best! By the time Isabella is in a position to work off her case, Mack will have had plenty of time getting his team up to speed."

I nodded in agreement, knowing Detective Mack was one of the best narcotic officers around and no doubt could get a team trained in a year. I said, "I'll most likely be back in patrol myself within a year and a half."

Lieutenant Pagh nodded. "Tommy, start working with Mack and see if you can get Isabella out here to interview her as soon as possible."

CHAPTER
43

For the next two weeks, I thoroughly went through Isabella Herrera's arrest reports by the FBI. I contacted her attorney, Ralph Glasing, and discussed the state drug trafficking charges we had on her. I said, "We have a very strong case against Isabella. She's looking at twenty-five years to life if she's convicted on all charges. Deputy District Attorney Scott Alexander is handling the case—You'll need to contact him. He works in the Major Narcotic Prosecuting Unit in downtown Los Angeles."

Several days later, I received a call from Deputy District Attorney Alexander. He said, "Glasing and I discussed the state prosecution case against Isabella. He fully understands the cases we have on his client and is aware she is looking at spending decades in the California state prison system." He continued, "Glasing asked about possibly working out a deal to reduce or get rid of the state's charges against Isabella. I told him to work with you about what could be done about her charges. In the meantime, keep me updated on any conversations you have with Isabella's attorney."

"Thanks, I will," I said.

Maybe at long last, I'd get to finally meet Isabella.

CHAPTER
44

Two weeks later, I had Isabella Herrera transferred to the Los Angeles County Jail, so we could interview her. While her attorney said she would agree to meet with us, he couldn't promise anything. It was Sergeant Tilly's idea to first transfer Isabella to the county jail for three days instead of the Torrance Police facility. He said, "Isabella's been pampered in the federal system—we need to soften her up. We must show her what the state prison system will be like if she doesn't cooperate. The federal penitentiary system is like Disneyland compared to the California state prison system."

Isabella Herrera was now sitting in a small cell in the Los Angeles County Jail. Detective Mack and I knew we only had one chance to get her to work with us. We met with Sergeant Tilly to help us come up with a game plan on how to interview her because we weren't dealing with an ordinary drug trafficker.

We knew Isabella Herrera was extremely intelligent. She ran one of the largest illicit drug distribution empires in the United States. She would be completely turned off by traditional police interviewing techniques, so we had to handle this with the utmost care. The best way to interview someone of her stature was to be frank and detail our knowledge of her business, and then present all the cases we had on her.

Three days later, Detective Mack and I had Isabella Herrera transferred from the Los Angeles County Jail to the Torrance Police

Department Jail. The jail staff placed her in one of our secure inter-view rooms, where she waited for us to arrive.

Detective Mack and I brought cheeseburgers, fries, and Cokes for all three of us to eat and get to know one another. From surveil-lances we had conducted on her, we knew she liked cheeseburgers and would appreciate the meal.

Detective Mack and I walked in the interview room with our lunches in hand. Isabella stood up and immediately reached her hand out and introduced herself. Detective Mack said, "I'm Detective Mack and this is Detective Greer. We've brought some lunch—hope-fully an improvement from the slop they serve in county."

Isabella was delighted with our lunch selection. "Thank you, I love a good cheeseburger," she said.

I looked directly at her and said, "I know you do."

Isabella looked at me, slightly tilted her head and asked, "How do you know that?"

"I'll show you what I'm talking about later."

As we ate, we made small talk. We talked about her stay in county jail and her family in Columbia. It was a great call by Sergeant Tilly to have her stay in county jail for three days because she hated it.

Detective Mack and I took notice of her beauty. She had flaw-less skin and long dark hair, but there was one thing that shook me to the core—she had dark-black, soulless eyes. When she looked at you, it was as if she was looking straight through you.

Isabella's English was perfect, which was a big bonus for us. Just from this short period of time, I could tell that she liked to control the conversation. It was easy to imagine her being the CEO of some Fortune 500 company and controlling every business deal.

When we finished lunch, I excused myself. "I'll be back in a few minutes." I left to retrieve six large four-inch casebook binders, which were entirely filled with all the cases involving Isabella and her organization. A jailer assisted me in carrying the casebooks to the interview room. As we entered, Isabella was just finishing up her meal. We placed all six casebooks in the middle of the table, and then I grabbed my chair, positioned it right next to her, and sat down.

The first thing I did was pull out a surveillance photograph of Isabella eating a cheeseburger at a restaurant adjacent to the U-Haul business where she rented the trailer in Anaheim. In the picture with her was her right-hand man, Santiago Ramirez—the person we nicknamed "the secretary."

Isabella placed her drink down on the table, picked up the photograph, and studied it. She looked at me, then at Detective Mack and shook her head. She asked, "How did you take this without me knowing?" I said nothing. I grabbed the first casebook and proceeded to open it.

Detective Mack explained, "We got leads from informants who pointed us in the right direction, to the right people, and to locations where we ended up taking people like you down. We took down their organizations by seizing large quantities of cocaine, marijuana, and money."

I said, "We never reveal these informants to anyone so don't bother asking."

Isabella looked at me and was processing what we had just explained to her. Detective Mack and I then took turns outlining the cases we had on her. We showed her the hundreds of pages of phone numbers from calls made from pay phones to pagers she and her employees used. Isabella was speechless. Then we showed her hundreds of surveillance photographs we had of her and her employees. She placed her hand over her mouth and spoke under her breath, "I can't believe this."

When Isabella looked at a surveillance photograph of herself leaving the restaurant in the Valley on Thanksgiving night with Santiago she exclaimed, "I knew I was being followed that night. I was right!"

I said, "The only reason you detected our surveillance was because it wasn't Detective Mack or our crew surveilling you. We had a lot of people to follow that night, so we went with Santiago because he drove in our direction. It was unfortunate that the surveillance crew that followed you had some inexperienced officers that were assisting. Santiago didn't have a clue he was followed home. Were you aware that he was arrested with a million dollars in his car?"

"I told—actually, I pleaded with Santiago and warned him that he was followed that night after dinner. Santiago insisted he hadn't been and wanted to stay put. He had a girlfriend coming in town and was only thinking of one thing—and it wasn't his work."

As we went through Isabella's casebooks, I showed her the newspaper article about her in the Michoacán newspaper. She responded, "I can't believe you have this. You guys have everything." For the next hour, she told us about how she fled to Mexico the night of the Thanksgiving dinner. She said, "I knew I was being followed, so I paid a lady five hundred dollars to drive me down to the border. I also knew that if I was being followed by the police, they'd never follow me into Mexico. If someone other than law enforcement followed me there, then that would've been a grave mistake on their part." Isabella then explained how she flew back to Colombia and met with the bosses.

I asked, "Who are your bosses?"

"I will never tell you."

She continued and detailed everything we already knew about Michoacán and the airstrip she used to transport tons of cocaine by aircraft from Colombia. She also verified what we already knew or surmised about what occurred while she was in Michoacán. She talked about her contact in Michoacán, Conrado Hernandez, who owned the airstrip she used. "He turned me in to the Federales to save his own neck," she said.

Isabella pointed to the news article about her escaping from the van transporting her to court. She sarcastically laughed at the part in which she allegedly hit the driver of the van over the head with her handcuffs, overpowered him, and escaped. She said, "What bullshit!"

At first, she contacted her people in Colombia to continue their shipments into the airstrip in Michoacán. "I had to do this because they were going to kill me if I didn't. When they figured out that I was being used by the people in Michoacán, they stopped the shipments. That was when the Federales came up with the story of me being arrested and escaping. All bullshit!" she said, raising her voice.

Isabella continued, "After a year of being held captive by Mexicans hired by the Federales, I told some guards that I had money

249

in Houston. I told them if they let me go, I would get a million dollars and bring it back to them. The Mexicans were stupid. They believed me and I fled to Houston, then I worked my way back to Colombia."

Once she was in Colombia, she took some time off before she was sent to New Jersey to coordinate a large cocaine deal. "That's when I was arrested," Isabella said. "I realized right away I was dealing with undercover cops. They didn't act like they were in the business, but it was too late. Several times, the FBI attempted to have me fly in a load of cocaine, but I refused because I knew who I was dealing with. I was just trying to limit my time behind bars."

We had been in the interview room for many hours now, so I told Isabella, "Let's take a break and continue this tomorrow."

She asked, "Do you know if I'm going to have to serve time in state prison after my time in federal custody?"

I replied, "Yes, twenty-five years to life if you're convicted on all charges. I know your attorney looked into your case and the charges against you. He's a smart man, so he wouldn't have told you to come here if we didn't have a solid case against you." I maintained eye contact with her and said, "You've seen the type of work we've done on your cases, and you can see how careful and thorough we are. If you decide to work with us, you'll walk out of the federal prison system a free woman. But, that's only if you decide to work with us. If you decide not to work with us, then after your federal prison time is up, you'll be transferred to the state prison system without seeing a day of freedom."

Isabella understood. "I have a nine-year-old daughter. If I do state time after my federal time, I'll miss seeing her grow up."

Detective Mack and I nodded in agreement.

I asked Isabella, "Where's your daughter?"

"My daughter's in a safe place."

I knew from her tone that her daughter was entirely off-limits.

Detective Mack asked, "Did you make up your mind? Do you want to work off your cases and walk away a free woman?"

"What choice do I really have? If I have to do state jail time, I'd only do it for the safety of my daughter and my family back home.

Now that I've seen your casebooks and the way you were able to surveil me and my organization without any of us noticing, I'm willing to take that chance—But, I'll only work with you two." She trusted us.

*****

The next morning, I picked up some breakfast and coffee at a local restaurant known for having the best breakfast burritos in town. On my way to the station, I called the jailers and told them to not feed Isabella and to take her back to the same interview room we used the day before.

When I arrived, Detective Mack met me with a big grin. "We got her," he said. I agreed, but we still had to break the news that I probably wouldn't be involved in her case, as I was leaving the undercover detail within a year or so. Detective Mack said, "Yeah, we're also going to have to tell her that our narcotic team won't be working on her case either, since most of them are leaving the team for promotions."

While Detective Mack wanted to continue to work in the undercover world of narcotics, he knew his entire team, including Sergeant Tilly and Lieutenant Pagh, were moving on. The new team would be good, but inexperienced. He also knew he didn't want to work with the new sergeant slated for the position.

Lieutenant Pagh was moving on to head up a multicity narcotic task force and asked Detective Mack to come along and run the team with him. Everyone on our narcotic team was an expert on Colombian drug cartels, but Detective Mack was the entire package.

Detective Mack asked, "How are we going to tell Isabella this and keep her trust in us?"

"Let me do the talking. I think I know how to keep her."

Detective Mack and I walked in the interview room where Isabella was seated in one of the steel chairs at the table. As we entered, she stood to shake our hands. We could tell we had made an impression on her. Now I hoped we could keep that impression after we told her about our upcoming changes. Having an informant of Isabella's stature and capabilities was a once-in-a-lifetime shot. We certainly didn't want to lose her, but we had to tell her the truth. We needed her buy-in.

I handed Isabella her breakfast burrito and coffee. As we ate, we talked about some of her cases and how she'd orchestrate everything from start to finish. I put my coffee down and began, "We need to discuss the future—project out—and come up with a realistic time-line for when you'll be transferred to a West Coast federal prison, so you can begin giving us cases."

I could see Isabella knew I was going to tell her something she wouldn't like. I said, "The earliest I could see you up and running for us is a year to a year and a half from now. Your federal prison time will be up in a little over three years. Your contract with us needs to be finished before your time in federal prison ends."

I continued, "The only people who know you're looking at state prison are the people in this room, our partners, your attorney, and the district attorney. If you don't fulfill your contract with us prior to your federal prison sentence ending, it will be a nightmare for you. Once you're transferred to a state prison, everyone in the world will know you have state charges on you and how long your sentence is. If for some reason you're released from state prison because you ful-filled your contract with us at this time, you and your family will be in grave danger."

"I understand. I have no problem fulfilling my contract while in federal custody. It will be much easier for me to get my part done if I'm in a federal prison located in the Western United States though," she said.

"I can and will get that done, but it will take a few months, maybe a year—"

Isabella was no dummy. She interrupted me and said, "What else is going on? I can tell you have more than this to tell me."

I looked at Detective Mack, then back at Isabella and contin-ued, "I'm leaving my current undercover detail in the near future."

Isabella shook her head and said, "No, no!"

I raised my voice and said, "Listen to me! Listen to what I have to say. It's all good—I promise you. Although I'm leaving, my boss,

Lieutenant Pagh, promised that I'd still be one of your contacts, along with Detective Mack." I paused for a couple of seconds, pointed to Isabella and said, "Wait one minute." I got up, stuck my head out of the interview room, and asked the jailer to contact Lieutenant Pagh ASAP and have him come to the interview room immediately. I closed the door, sat down again, and said, "I want to introduce you to my boss, Lieutenant Pagh. He is the man. He gets things done around here. He knows we have a great opportunity to make some big cases if you work with us while you're in federal custody. He's the one who sent me down to Del Rio, Texas, to work with the DEA. That's where we found the cocaine trail you used from Colombia to the landing strip in Michoacán, through Del Rio, Texas, and into the Western United States." I continued, "Within the next year, the Torrance narcotic team will have all new personnel." Isabella again shook her head in protest. I said, "Look, I don't have to tell you this. I could keep quiet and let other less experienced people attempt to work off your case and put you and your family in danger. I can't do that—not only to you, but more importantly to your family, who have nothing to do with this. The timing couldn't be better. Detective Mack, who you know from reviewing our cases on you, is the best at what he does." I pointed to Mack and said, "This man trained me, and I'm still learning from him. Lieutenant Pagh and Detective Mack are joining a multicity narcotic task force, and Lieutenant Pagh will be in charge of it. Detective Mack will run the new team. He will have about a year or more to train the new detectives and he'll handpick them himself."

Right then, there was a knock on the door. I opened the door to find Lieutenant Pagh. I asked him to come in and introduced him to Isabella. She stood and reached out to shake his hand with the same confidence she had when she shook mine the first time I interviewed her. Lieutenant Pagh, with his usual charisma, told Isabella to take a seat as he grabbed a seat at the table. Lieutenant Pagh said, "Thank you for filling in the blanks regarding our cases and the inner work-ings of the drug trade here in Southern California."

Prior to coming to work this particular morning, I phoned Lieutenant Pagh and informed him of our dilemma in telling Isabella about the changes coming to our narcotic team. I was sure Lieutenant Pagh had an approach on how he was going to convince Isabella she was in good hands.

Lieutenant Pagh said, "I'm sure Detectives Greer and Mack have told you about the upcoming changes with the narc team. They're heading elsewhere in their careers. I'm sure you can appreciate that." He looked right at Isabella with a wide grin on his face and said, "But Detective Mack and I will be with you, and Detective Greer will stay in contact with you. The new task force that we're putting together will be second to none." Lieutenant Pagh reiterated his comment to reassure her, "We'll be more than capable—I promise you that!"

For the first time, Isabella smiled. She sat back in her chair and said, "Let's do it!"

Isabella then sat right back up and her smile disappeared from her face. "One thing you should know, I will never turn in a Columbian—not even if they're my enemy. I have many paybacks against the Mexicans who turned me in to the Michoacán Federales and held me captive."

Lieutenant Pagh replied, "I don't care who you turn in. As long as we get the drugs off the streets—we'll be happy."

Before leaving, Lieutenant Pagh shook Isabella's hand and reassured her that she was in good hands. I said, "I'll contact the district attorney who's handling your case and tell him to write up a contract that you and your attorney will be happy with."

Isabella asked, "How long will it take?"

"I hope to complete the contract this afternoon, and I'll send it to your attorney by tomorrow. Your attorney will meet with you and go over it right away. Once you agree to it, we will meet with the superior court judge handling your case and he'll have to approve it. If everything goes smoothly, we'll have everything completed within three days."

Isabella asked, "Can I stay here instead of being transferred back to county jail?" I agreed and felt it would be best.

Detective Mack looked across the table at Isabella. "I need to ask you a question."

"Yes, of course," she said.

"When you spoke of not turning in any of your Colombian drug traffickers, you spoke with such hatred for the Mexicans. Does this hate come from how you were treated while being held captive in Mexico?"

Isabella became solemn and replied, "Yes."

"Did they physically assault you?"

Isabella stared straight ahead. You could see the pain on her face and that said it all.

I broke the silence and said, "Either I or Detective Mack will touch base with you later this evening."

For the rest of the day, Detective Mack and I worked with District Attorney Scott Alexander from the Major Narcotic Prosecution Unit in downtown Los Angeles regarding Isabella's contract. We informed him that we felt two large seizures would be sufficient. The contract stipulated that Isabella had to provide us a ton of cocaine and a $1 million money seizure from the sale of cocaine. District Attorney Alexander wrote up the contract and forwarded it to Isabella's attorney.

The next morning, Isabella's attorney met with us at the Torrance Police Department. Then he met with Isabella by himself, and she agreed to the contract. I then informed District Attorney Alexander the contract was a go. Alexander set up an appointment with the superior court judge handling Isabella's case for the following morning at ten o'clock in the judge's chambers.

The next day, Isabella's attorney, District Attorney Alexander, Detective Mack, and I met with the superior court judge at the criminal courthouse in downtown Los Angeles. There was no need for Isabella to be there, as her attorney was representing her interest. More importantly, we didn't want anyone who might know Isabella to see her at a state courthouse, let alone inside a judge's chambers. It wouldn't take a genius to figure out why she was there—to work with law enforcement.

District Attorney Alexander, a highly respected attorney, introduced all of us to the superior court judge. There was a quiet, cold demeanor in the room. The judge was all business and no one talked unless spoken to. District Attorney Alexander had given the judge the contract the day before, so he could review it before our meeting.

The judge asked Detective Mack and I a few questions regarding Isabella's cases. His eyebrows raised when we gave him the *Reader's Digest* version of her background and the amount of cocaine and money laundering seizures we confiscated over the last five years. The judge asked Isabella's attorney several questions regarding her background and if Isabella fully understood what the contract meant. Her attorney acknowledged that she was fully aware of what she was doing, but also made the judge aware that if at any time Isabella felt she was putting her family in danger, she'd back out of the contract and serve her time. The judge signed the contract and asked us all to do the same.

It was set. We agreed to make a couple of narcotic deals happen while Isabella was in federal custody. All I needed to do now was get Isabella transferred to a West Coast federal prison. Detective Mack, Isabella's attorney, and I responded back to the Torrance jail to inform her it was a go. Isabella signed the contract and I forwarded it to District Attorney Alexander who filed it with the court and sealed it to protect its confidentiality.

Mack then gave Isabella our teams safety deposit box address we used for our undercover operations. Mack told Isabella to use this address to forward letters to us. She then asked that when we wrote letters to her, to pretend we were family, and under no circumstances were we to discuss drug deals.

She said, "The guards read all letters coming in and out of prison. There are certain guards that will hold something like me working with the cops over my head." She had witnessed it firsthand. "I've seen guards blackmail inmates and threaten to tell the other inmates they were a snitch if they didn't do favors for them."

Detective Mack asked, "What favors?"

"Everything from sex to money and cigarettes."

Isabella continued, "If I want you to meet someone on the outside regarding a drug deal, I'll write that a cousin, aunt, or uncle will be in town and want to meet you at a certain restaurant or something like that. We'll need to make the letters as vague as possible. I'll also give your pager numbers to people, so they can contact you." Then she added, "When you come and visit, come as a close friend or relative, because the guards and other inmates will see me talking to you."

Detective Mack said, "We understand. Is there anything else we need to know?"

Isabella only had one question. "How long before I'm transferred to a prison on the West Coast?"

I responded, "The federal government moves at a snail's pace, so it could be up to a year. But it's alright because by then, Detective Mack and Lieutenant Pagh will have had plenty of time getting their new team in order. But right now, we've got some things to square away, so we'll get going."

For the next couple of months, I wrestled with the red tape to get Isabella transferred to a West Coast federal prison. Things were happening slowly, but I kept working on it while working cases with the narcotic team. It was challenging as most of us were also getting ready to go back in uniform patrol. Lieutenant Pagh and Detective Mack had been reassigned to the multicity narcotic task force which meant I rarely saw them. I was the one who usually checked the undercover post office box for mail from Isabella.

She was sending letters, but there was nothing of significance. Isabella was just maintaining a pattern of letters to and from me, so the prison guards who screened the mail wouldn't see a strange new name on a letter when potential cases started rolling in. All letters from Isabella ended with a picture of a heart with a happy face in the middle. They were then added to the casebook I had created for her. Each time a letter arrived, I let Detective Mack know Isabella had sent her regards.

CHAPTER
45

In addition to taking over the multicity task force, Lieutenant Pagh was still in charge of our team until the department picked a replacement. Many changes were happening within the Torrance Police Department.

The new chief's policing philosophy and non-proactive policing style couldn't have been more different from what our men and women were used to. This caused a domino effect at every rank level in the department. The changes it had on our undercover details, our narcotic and crime impact teams, were significant.

One such change was everyone in the narcotic team left the detail. These detectives were the cream of the crop. Most were hard chargers and future leaders of the department. During our tenure, our team arrested hundreds of drug cartel members, including Isabella Herrera, the Columbian cocaine queenpin. This team was also responsible for seizing tons of cocaine and marijuana, millions of dollars in cash, and numerous properties; including houses, trucks, and cars from Colombian drug cartels. Our accomplishments would never be matched by any department our size. Sergeant Tilly was promoted to lieutenant and was reassigned back to patrol division. Shortly after, the rest of our narcotic team and I also transitioned back to uniform patrol.

Lieutenant Pagh was clever. By highlighting his accomplishments from the past decade, he convinced the Torrance Police

Department and city leaders that with an incoming inexperienced young narcotic team, it would be in the city's best interest to reassign him and Detective Mack to this new outside task force. He emphasized that they would continue to bring in millions from asset forfeiture seizures to the city's coffers, while the new Torrance narcotic team learned the ropes. The hope was when the new Torrance narcotic team got up to speed, the department and the city would obtain revenues from asset forfeiture cases from both Lieutenant Pagh's task force and the city of Torrance's narcotic team.

Sergeant Tilly's replacement, Sergeant Elker, had very little narcotic experience when it came to the Colombian cartels. It was like fitting a square peg in a round hole. In fairness to Sergeant Elker, neither he nor anyone else could match Sergeant Tilly's knowledge, accomplishments, or leadership. They were huge shoes to fill!

To be a successful narcotic detective or supervisor working major Colombian drug cartel cases, one must have the right demeanor. Sergeant Elker certainly did not. He had a type A personality and expected immediate results. When working major narcotic investigations, like Colombian drug cartels, one needs a lot of patience because some cases take months, or even years, to conclude.

For the next year, Sergeant Elker's team didn't make any significant seizures. He scrambled to get that big case to make a name for himself. One day, one of his narcotic detectives informed him about a case I had with our informant, Isabella Herrera. Sergeant Elker saw this as a huge opportunity.

The next morning, I was approached by one of Sergeant Elker's detectives, Detective Baker, in the hallway in the downstairs portion of the police department. Detective Baker and I engaged in small talk, but I could tell something was off, as he appeared nervous. He said, "Sergeant Elker heard about the Isabella Herrera case. He says he wants it."

I was shocked. I said, "There's no way in hell Sergeant Elker or his inexperienced narcotic team will ever work the Isabella Herrera case. It's too complex. Besides, Detective Mack has it, and he and his task force are working with her." Detective Baker said he would relay the information to Sergeant Elker and walked away.

Deep down I knew that a confrontation with Sergeant Elker was going to happen in a matter of time. Before that happened, Detective Mack and I had one more adventure in the prosecution of a large-scale narcotic case.

CHAPTER
46

It had been nearly a year since I had seen Detective Mack. He was buried working on the task force with Lieutenant Pagh. A month earlier, Detective Mack and I were contacted by a Deputy District Attorney, Harris, in Stockton, California. Harris advised us that he was prosecuting a major narcotic case that was going to trial soon. He related that he was trying eight defendants in one of the biggest cocaine busts the county had seen in years. He went on to say, "As a matter of fact, one of the defendants, Rodrigo Hernandez, was the Mexican kingpin of Stockton."

Harris said, "Rodrigo Hernandez has evaded prosecution for years because he was so isolated and protected within his organization. But I think we have a pretty good case on him and his coconspirators for cocaine trafficking." Deputy District Attorney Harris added, "I learned that one of your Colombian drug cartel cases might be related to Rodrigo Hernandez."

Deputy District Attorney Harris suspected that Hernandez was getting his shipments of cocaine from a Riverside case we had. He said, "The markings on the kilos of cocaine from my case match the markings of kilos from your Riverside case." He also said he believed an attorney, and a wanted suspect in our Riverside case, was involved in supplying his defendant with cocaine for years.

I said, "I'll pull out my casebooks and see if there are any more details I can tie in from our Riverside case to yours." After getting off the phone, I pulled out three four-inch binder casebooks. Besides recovering cocaine, we had recovered pay-and-owe sheets from the house of the drug-dealing attorney. I remembered because the pay-and-owe sheets were very detailed, like the kind an attorney would have maintained, and contained the names and locations of who he supplied his cocaine to, the amounts, and how much he was owed.

As I reviewed the pay-and-owe sheets recovered by Detective Mack, I noticed large amounts of cocaine were delivered to a Rodrigo Hernandez in Stockton, California. I laughed knowing Deputy District Attorney Harris was going to love this information. The unfortunate thing was, I also knew Detective Mack and I would be subpoenaed to testify in this case. I told Deputy District Attorney Harris what I had found. He was excited and thanked me. He also said, "You and Detective Mack should expect to see your subpoenas in the mail shortly."

The day before Detective Mack and I were leaving for Stockton, California, to testify in the narcotic case, Detective Baker contacted me again regarding Isabella Herrera's case. He said Sergeant Elker wanted to talk to me in his office. I said, "Tell Sergeant Elker I'll be there within fifteen minutes."

I entered Sergeant Elker's office and closed the door. I knew our conversation wasn't going to go well, and I didn't want others to hear us talking.

Sergeant Elker said, "I want you to turn over the Isabella Herrera file and case to me."

I asked, "What for?"

"My narcotic team is going to work the case."

I shook my head. "I can't—That's not possible. You and your team are too inexperienced to work such a high-level Colombian drug cartel informant—"

"I want the case today," he demanded before I finished my thought.

"Not a chance. If your team works this case, you and your crew will burn the case into the ground and get Isabella Herrera and her family killed."

Sergeant Elker raised his voice. "Who cares about her? She's a crook—"

I interrupted him and raised my voice to match his. "Correct, but her nine-year-old daughter and family aren't, and they're the ones who'll pay the price for your errors."

"Tommy, you need to hand over Isabella's case file."

"Absolutely not. Detective Mack has the file anyway, and he will continue to work the case."

Sergeant Elker clenched his jaw, stared me down and said, "Isabella Herrera is a Torrance case. It belongs to me."

"Even if I turn it over to you, she won't work with you."

"How do you know that?"

I explained, "Detective Mack and I flipped her by showing her the type of cases we had put together by following her—she was impressed because she had never detected us. She told us she wouldn't work with anyone else because she only trusted us." I glared at Sergeant Elker, "Are we done here?"

"Yes, but this isn't over."

I opened the door and walked out of his office knowing he was probably right, this wasn't over.

*****

It was a Tuesday afternoon, and I was excited knowing that I would be spending the next five hours in the same car with Detective Mack. We hadn't seen each other in almost a year. We had talked many times about Isabella and I was forwarding her letters to him, but I hadn't seen him. The timing was perfect for us to meet, as Isabella had just been transferred to a federal prison facility in Seattle, Washington.

Detective Mack picked me up at the Torrance Police Department, and we drove his undercover car to Stockton, California. During the drive we caught up on our lives; personal and professional. I kidded him about gaining a few pounds since I last saw him, and he laughed it off. The life of a narcotic detective working major cases required long hours coupled with a fast-food diet—not the best formula for a supermodel body.

I told Detective Mack how Sergeant Elker was pushing to get Isabella's case. Mack scoffed, "That would be disastrous. Sergeant Elker's narcotic team isn't remotely capable of handling such a case." While the narcotic members on his team were young, sharp, and excellent cops; having a leader with Sergeant Elker's personality wasn't a good fit. The saying "You're only as good as your leader" was true in this case.

I told Detective Mack to hold on to Isabella's case, and we could make plans to visit her soon. He said, "I'm sure Isabella is ready to get her case over with."

Our drive seemed quick, as we talked and caught up. When we got close to Stockton, I pulled out our Thomas Guide and found directions to the Holiday Inn we were staying at. Deputy District Attorney Harris set us up there and we were meeting him for dinner at 8:00 p.m. We checked into our rooms, showered, and met 30 minutes later in the hotel restaurant.

As we waited for Deputy District Attorney Harris, we both ordered a beer at the bar. Mack looked around the restaurant and bar and asked, "How do we know what Harris looks like?"

I laughed, "I have no clue."

About two beers later, an old-timer with salt-and-pepper hair, wearing a wrinkled suit and snakeskin cowboy boots approached and asked, "Are you the boys from Torrance?"

Mack and I both responded simultaneously, "Yes, we are!"

The old-timer stuck his hand out and said, "John Harris, Deputy District Attorney, thanks for coming. Are you boys hungry?"

We laughed, "Starving!"

He gestured to an isolated table in the back of the restaurant and said, "Let's sit there for privacy."

We sat and he thanked us again for driving up to Stockton and being willing to testify in his case. Harris said, "It'll be a jury trial. The jury has already been selected, and they'll be sequestered until the trial is concluded."

I asked, "Isn't that a little too much, sequestering a jury for a drug trafficking case?"

Harris nodded in agreement but advised, "We don't have our normal defendants standing trial in this case."

Harris went on to explain the history of the city of Stockton and how the main defendant, Rodrigo Hernandez, and his family had been in charge of the drug trade for decades. He said, "The Hernandez family is very powerful. They have used everything from intimidation to murder to get their point across." Deputy District Attorney Harris enlightened us that this court case was no different. He said, "So far, the word on the street is there's a hit out on me and some of our arresting officers. When I added both of you to the witness list, I found your names on the hit list as well!"

Detective Mack laughed and jokingly said, "Good thing I have all my weapons with me."

Deputy District Attorney Harris said, "I'm not too worried about being taken out by Hernandez's people, but just in case, it's legal for me to carry a firearm. In fact, I have one on me right now." He added, "The most recent information is that Rodrigo Hernandez's people are going to storm the courthouse tomorrow morning and overtake it to help Hernandez escape. This might sound like a movie, but Hernandez and his family are very dangerous. The Stockton Police Department is taking all precautions available."

Deputy District Attorney Harris took the next thirty minutes to tell us what he would ask us on the stand. Detective Mack and I had testified hundreds of times in our careers, and this case seemed no different. In fact, when Deputy District Attorney Harris excused himself to use the restroom, Mack and I looked at each other and commented on why we were even needed for this case. He already had a pretty solid case on his defendants. Our case just showed that his defendant received shipments of cocaine from a guy we had a case on. Detective Mack looked at me and said, "Oh well. It gets us away from our regular work for a couple days."

When Deputy District Attorney Harris returned to the table, he asked if we had any questions. I asked, "What time do you want us at the courthouse in the morning?"

Harris said, "Because of the death threats against you guys, you'll be escorted to the courthouse by Stockton's SWAT team."

Detective Mack and I both smiled and said, "You got it."

Harris told us to be in the hotel lobby at 8:30 a.m. "You won't miss the guys who'll be escorting you."

Mack and I both laughed and shook Harris's hand and said, "See you in the morning."

Since it was only 9:30 p.m., Detective Mack and I sat down at the hotel bar and had a few more beers. An hour later, I was tired and went up to bed. Mack said he was tired too but had some "brown water" in his room and wanted a nightcap before he went to bed. He and I walked to the elevator, and before getting in, I took a good look around to make sure no one was following us. We pressed the third-floor button and headed up.

The elevator door opened, and we walked out slowly, looking in both directions. Deputy District Attorney Harris had gotten to us a little, and we made sure no one got the drop on us. Our rooms were across the hall from each other. I unlocked my door, but before I entered, I looked back and told Detective Mack, "I'll knock on your door in the morning. We'll head out together."

*****

The following morning, I got up at seven and had breakfast downstairs in the hotel restaurant. There were very few people in the lobby and restaurant. I quickly ate and headed back to my room. As a precaution, I took the stairs.

It was a jury trial, so Detective Mack and I brought our suits and ties in an attempt to look professional. At about 8:15 a.m. I called Detective Mack's room and asked him if he was ready. He told me to come over. When he opened the door, I took a step back and stared in disbelief at the suit he was wearing.

Laughing, I asked, "Dude, when was the last time you put that on?"

Mack laughed and admitted, "It's been some time."

"Man, I told you—You've gained some weight. You're popping out of that thing!"

"Shut up! My suit fits fine."

We were still laughing as we took the stairs down to the lobby. I carried the three large Riverside casebooks, just in case the court or attorneys wanted to see them.

When Detective Mack and I reached the lobby, we saw a crowd of onlookers staring out the glass entrance doors. On the other side were four large SWAT team members from Stockton, fully dressed in their fatigues with weapons at the ready. Mack looked at me and said, "You've got to be kidding me!" Both of us had been involved in some big cases in our careers—against some very dangerous people—but we had never been escorted to court.

We approached the SWAT guys and identified ourselves, verbally and by identification. The SWAT sergeant, Sergeant Rocker, introduced himself, shook our hands and said, "Let's go."

Detective Mack asked, "Can we just follow you guys to the courthouse in our own car?"

Sergeant Rocker shook his head, "No, sorry, those are not my orders. We'll drive you in our police cruisers."

We certainly weren't going to argue with the sergeant, so we walked over to the middle of three police cars. The first and third cars contained two heavily armed SWAT personnel. Sergeant Rocker pointed to the back seat of the middle car and asked us to get in. I laughed at Detective Mack as he waddled and squirmed to get into the back of the police car because his pants were so tight. "Shut up!" he said while laughing.

In the car with us were the sergeant and another SWAT officer. Sergeant Rocker was in the front passenger seat and was on his police radio, coordinating our ride to the courthouse. Mack looked at me and commented, "Now I know how the president of the United States feels."

We arrived at the courthouse and were escorted to a side entrance. At the doors of the side entrance were several more fully armed SWAT personnel. We were then led up to the fifth-floor courtroom. It was eerie seeing fully armed SWAT officers at every stairwell entrance and in the hallway of the fifth floor. Obviously, these guys were taking the death threats and the escape attempt seriously.

Detective Mack and I entered the courtroom and let Deputy District Attorney Harris know we were there. Harris smiled at us and shook Mack's hand, as mine were full with the three large casebooks. Harris asked, "Can you two meet me in the hallway?" As we walked out of the courtroom, I could see it was packed—each and every chair was taken. The majority of the people in the courtroom were Hispanic. All of them stared us down as we entered and exited the courtroom. All eight of the defendants were Mexican, so I was assuming all the ugly stares were from relatives or friends of defendants.

Deputy District Attorney Harris said, "The judge will start the trial promptly at 9:30 a.m. He is very fair and he runs his courtroom with an iron fist. He won't let attorneys control the court, and he's not keen on interruptions in his courtroom." Detective Mack and I both nodded in acknowledgment.

Deputy District Attorney Harris looked at me and said, "You're up first." He reminded us, "There are eight defendants and each one has their own attorney. You guys saw the courtroom. It's standing room only." He smiled at us and said, "It should be a good one!" Mack and I were both thinking the same thing. We weren't sure what Harris expected, but we were here to do what we were asked to do.

The court bailiff stepped into the hallway and told Deputy District Attorney Harris the judge was about ready. Harris pointed to us and said, "Wait out here until I call you." He returned to the courtroom with the court bailiff right behind him.

When Harris was out of earshot, Detective Mack asked me, "Is it me, or is that the same wrinkled suit Harris was wearing last night?"

I laughed and told Mack, "At least it fits him."

We both started laughing. I said, "Any deputy district attorney wearing those old snakeskin cowboy boots must be an icon around here."

At that moment, the courtroom doors opened and the court bailiff, along with Deputy District Attorney Harris, appeared. Harris looked at me and said, "Game time, Tommy." As I walked into the courtroom, I noticed there were eight armed bailiffs standing near the eight defendants. The judge waved me up to the witness stand.

A female court deputy administered the oath, swearing me to tell the truth. I then sat down in the witness chair, as I had so many times in my career. I unbuttoned my coat, took a deep breath and acknowledged the judge. I then scanned the room, smiled at the jury, looked at the deputy district attorney, and glanced to my right at all eight defendants and their eight attorneys sitting next to them. Never in my career had I been involved in such a high-profile court case with so many defendants.

I watched Deputy District Attorney Harris as he stood and appeared to be gathering his thoughts. It seemed like a Hollywood movie set, not a courtroom. I looked at this old-timer, Deputy District Attorney Harris, and his unusual wardrobe—his wrinkled suit, bushy salt-and-pepper hair and big snakeskin cowboy boots. I almost laughed watching him as he approached me at the witness stand.

Deputy District Attorney Harris asked me some standard questions; like my occupation and years on the job. He then paused, and asked the judge if the court could hear the witness's—referring to me—voir dire. I had been through the voir dire process many times in my career, demonstrating my qualification as an expert witness in state and federal courts.

The judge told Deputy District Attorney Harris to proceed. Harris looked at me, then at the jury, then back at me and asked, "Can you please explain to the jury and to the court your expertise?" I responded by outlining my career, my training, and my expertise regarding drug possession, possession of drugs for sale and drug trafficking. I told the court I had been involved in the seizures of more than five tons of cocaine and marijuana, along with seizures of more than $10 million of United States currency from the sale of cocaine.

I further explained, "I've been recognized as an expert in state and federal courts regarding the inner workings of major narcotic organizations, specifically that of the Colombian drug cartels."

At this point, all eight attorneys for the defendants literally leaped up in unison screaming "Objection! Objection!" to the judge.

The courtroom erupted in chaos with all defendants' attorneys yelling at once, along with some of the family members in the audience.

The judge, known for running a tightly monitored courtroom, had lost all control. He was pounding his gavel and shouting for the courtroom to come to order. One of the defendants' attorneys was screaming, "Objection. These Colombian hit men from Los Angeles are linking our clients to the Colombian drug cartels? Objection!" He was referring to Detective Mack and I as Colombian hit men. We had been called a lot of names, but never that.

The judge was livid at all the commotion. He ordered the bailiffs to immediately remove the jurors. The chaos only lasted a few minutes, but it felt like an hour. I looked at old Deputy District Attorney Harris as he walked back to his seat at the end of a table facing the court bench. As the commotion continued, he sat back in his chair, crossed his legs showing his snakeskin cowboy boots, interlocked his hands behind his neck, looked directly at me, and winked. Right then, I got it.

He had planned this all along. He wanted the jury to hear and understand that Detective Mack and I specialized in the Colombian drug cartels, and we were indeed experts in this area. He knew that even if the judge told the jurors to strike my testimony about the Colombian drug cartels, the damage was done, and the jurors would link these defendants to them.

I grinned at Harris and thought, *What a cagey move by this old-timer.* Watching him was like watching the TV series *Matlock* played by Andy Griffith. Harris, with his easygoing country boy demeanor, had fooled everyone. In reality, he was a calculated assassin in the courtroom. I loved it!

After the jury was removed, the defendants' attorneys argued against my testimony, which linked their clients to Colombian drug cartels. The judge listened to all eight defense attorneys' arguments, which took quite some time. He then ruled in Deputy District Attorney Harris's favor because I was just telling the court about my expertise, not specifically linking their clients to Colombian drug cartels. After the judge's ruling, the jury was brought back in the courtroom and I finished my testimony. The judge then excused me from the witness stand, and I left the courtroom.

When I walked out, Detective Mack was standing in the corridor, He said, "Wow! What the hell happened in there? I heard nothing but yelling."

I laughed and said, "Harris is my new hero."

Mack gave me a weird look, wondering what I was talking about.

Right then, Detective Mack, holding one of the heavy casebooks, bent down to set it on the floor while I was bending down to pick up one of the other case books. As we bent down simultaneously, Mack's head was literally three inches in proximity from mine. In the silence, we heard *rrrrrrrrrrrip.*

Mack looked up at me from our crouched positions and said, "No way!"

I started laughing and said, "Yes way! You just ripped your pants!"

We both stood up and Mack turned around. I lost it. His pants were ripped from back to front, and his tighty-whities were hanging out. Right then, the doors to the courtroom opened, and Deputy District Attorney Harris appeared and pointed to Detective Mack and said, "You're up!" Again, I burst out laughing. Harris looked at me, then at Mack and asked, "What's wrong?"

I pointed toward Mack's pants and said, "He just ripped his pants wide open!"

Harris started laughing with me as the court bailiff came out, pointed to Detective Mack and said, "Let's go!" Detective Mack pulled his jacket down behind him as he walked leaning backwards into the courtroom.

When Detective Mack came back from testifying, he was bright red. He said he had to walk to the whiteboard next to the jurors and make a drawing to note where he had located the cocaine and pay-and-owe sheets in our Riverside case. Mack said he tried leaning back hoping his jacket would cover the rip, so the jurors couldn't see his underwear.

Deputy District Attorney Harris came out of the courtroom, shook our hands and said, "Thanks boys. You two are dismissed for the day." He was laughing as hard as I was.

I asked the SWAT sergeant to give us a ride back to our hotel. Once there, Detective Mack and I went to our rooms and changed in to some shorts and T-shirts. We packed our overnight bags and checked out.

On the five-hour drive home, I told Detective Mack that I had been checking the post office box for letters from Isabella. I said, "We haven't received any letters from her in two weeks. It's not like her—She usually writes every week."

"That is unusual. Let's follow up in the next couple weeks," he said.

When Mack dropped me off at my car in the parking lot of the Torrance Police Department, he smiled and said, "I know you won't tell anyone about the ripped pants."

I laughed and said, "You can count on it!"

CHAPTER
47

During the first month back in uniform patrol, I started my morning shift by checking the post office box for letters from Isabella. There continued to be none. I called Detective Mack, "Any chance you've been to the post office box and grabbed any letters from Isabella? I still haven't seen any."

"No, something must be wrong, or maybe Isabella has decided not to work off her case."

"If you've got some time, you should fly to Seattle and visit her to find out what the heck is going on," I suggested.

"I'll discuss it with Lieutenant Pagh."

The next week started like any other. One morning as I was filling up my patrol car at the gas pumps in the station parking lot, Sergeant Finley, who had replaced Lieutenant Dalton as the new sergeant of the crime impact team, saw me and stopped. He was known as an excellent street cop and a top-notch investigator. Most people were intimidated by him, as he was a large man—six foot three, 250-plus pounds—with dark-black hair and a scraggly beard. He looked like an NFL player and was known for being very straightforward.

Sergeant Finley rolled his window down and said, "Hey, I want to warn you about Sergeant Elker. He's saying a lot of crappy things about you. I was just in a meeting with several sergeants, lieutenants, some captains, and the chief. Elker took the opportunity to talk very negatively about you in front of everyone."

I looked at Sergeant Finley and said, "You know what that's about, don't you?"

"Yeah, I know it's about the informant."

"Sergeant Elker is determined to make my life miserable."

Sergeant Finley said, "I think it's nonsense because it's all lies, so I wanted to warn you to watch your back."

I thanked Sergeant Finley and he drove away.

*****

It was the end of my shift when dispatch broadcast over the police radio that Lieutenant Lewis wanted to see me in his office. I acknowledged and drove to the station right away. Lieutenant Lewis had taken Lieutenant Pagh's position and was the division commander in charge of both the narcotic and crime impact undercover teams. Lieutenant Lewis, like Sergeant Elker, was a fish out of water in his current position. He was oblivious about what it took to be a proactive street cop, let alone an investigator. Now he oversaw one of the most important investigative positions in the department.

As I walked to Lieutenant Lewis's office, I had a bad feeling in my gut. I greeted our secretary, Kathy, and noticed there were no detectives at their desks. This was unusual, so I was sure Lieutenant Lewis told everyone to leave before I arrived.

Lieutenant Lewis said, "Close the door behind you."

I said to myself, *Here we go*, as I closed the door.

"Take a seat," he added.

"No thanks. I'm good standing," I said.

"Suit yourself."

He then pulled out six letters addressed to me from Isabella Herrera. I noticed that the envelopes had been opened which meant they had probably been read. Lieutenant Lewis was avoiding eye contact. He stuttered as he said, "Tommy, after reading these letters, it's clear to me you are too close and possibly having an affair with your informant, Isabella."

I stood there in shock. "What? Show me anywhere in her letters that would cause you to believe I'm having an affair with someone who's in prison."

Lieutenant Lewis took out one of the letters and pointed to the heart with a happy face inside. He said, "It's obvious you two have more than a professional relationship. I've discussed this with the chief already. If you don't hand over the Isabella Herrera case file to me, I'll open a personnel complaint against you for having an affair with an informant."

I stared right at him shaking my head. "So this is what you and Sergeant Elker have come up with to get Isabella's case? This is unbelievable! You don't have any idea—Isabella won't work for anyone other than me or Detective Mack."

Lieutenant Lewis stood up and said, "You have to the end of the day to hand over Isabella's case file, or I'll file a personnel complaint."

"I don't even have her case file—Detective Mack has it."

Lieutenant Lewis pushed again. "You have till the end of the day."

I said nothing, turned, and walked out of his office. As I went past Kathy, she whispered, "I'm so sorry, Tommy." I gave her a half smile as I rushed by.

I felt like I had been stabbed in my gut. I was angry and upset. Lieutenant Lewis and Sergeant Elker were so desperate to get a big case that they'd do anything to get one. Torrance had one of the biggest informants law enforcement could have asked for, and these two were willing to throw it away because of their egos.

I was accused of having an affair with a woman who had been in federal prison the entire time I had known her. I only had a couple of in-person meetings with Isabella and each time, I had a partner with me. Every meeting had been in our jail or the Los Angeles County lock-up. I knew that if I fought this allegation, I would win, but my reputation would be dragged through the mud for an entire year, not to mention the effect it would have on my family. In the meantime, these two would be given the case anyway.

I needed to get to an isolated area immediately. I went to the only place I knew to go, where no one would bother me. I went down to a restroom in the basement of the station, I opened a bathroom stall, fell to the ground, and puked. My body was aching. I sat in the stall for a while and attempted to gain control of myself. Unbeknownst to me, Lieutenant Dalton and Detective Riggs from the old crime impact team found out what happened. I assumed they had heard from Kathy because she loved our old teams and always kept a close eye out for us.

Suddenly I heard the bathroom door swing open and Lieutenant Dalton and Detective Riggs called out to me. I hesitated, but knew they wouldn't leave until I said something. "I just need some time alone," I said. I was sure they heard the anguish in my voice.

Detective Riggs yelled, "Fuck!" and walked back out the door. He wasn't just a partner; he was also a friend. We had known each other since high school, and he hated to see me in such pain.

Lieutenant Dalton said, "Hang in there, Tommy. This isn't over."

"Yes, it is. I'm done. I'm giving them the case. They're attacking my personal life now."

Lieutenant Dalton left me alone.

After an hour of sitting in the stall, I was finally able to compose myself, changed out of my uniform, and called Detective Mack. I filled him in with what was happening. He said, "I can't believe it— Do they understand Isabella won't work for them?"

"They don't give a damn. They have no idea what they're doing."

"They'll find out pretty quick. She's going to tell them to fuck off."

"Can we meet? I need to get Isabella's case file. I have to give it to Lieutenant Lewis by the end of the day."

"Yeah, meet me in the north end of the courthouse next to the department, and I'll have it for you."

Thirty minutes later, I met with Detective Mack. "Thanks for everything, Mack. I wish things had worked out."

"Yeah, me too Tommy."

He handed me Isabella's file, and I walked back to the station. When I arrived, I was approached by a couple buddies who worked in the traffic division. They told me they had just heard the rumor that I was having an affair with an informant. I was pissed. I knew the rumor would spread, but never did I think it would be this fast. "It's all lies," I said as I walked away.

When I got to the narcotic and crime impact office, Kathy was typing on her keyboard. She looked up at me, then at the case file in my hand. She asked, "Do you want me to take that Tommy? So you don't have to see Lieutenant Lewis?"

"Thank you, but I'll give it to him."

Kathy looked directly at me and whispered, "Be careful. Try not to say anything that will get you in trouble."

I looked at her and said, "You know—I don't care anymore."

Lieutenant Lewis's door was open, and he was sitting behind his big desk. I walked in and said, "Here's the case file you wanted." He didn't respond. I looked at him and in a low, calm voice said, "Lieutenant, you know what Isabella Herrera is going to tell you guys when you talk to her?"

He looked at me and again didn't respond.

I dropped the case file on his desk and said, "Fuck you guys!" I turned and walked out, passing Kathy, who now had tears in her eyes. I winked at her and grinned. It felt good to say that.

During the next week, there were a few more officers who approached me and told me they had heard the rumor. I was devastated knowing that these lies were superseding many years of hard work. I felt that I had better get out in front of the rumor, go home, and tell my wife. The last thing I wanted was for Nicole to hear it from somebody else.

When I got home, I found Nicole cooking dinner in the kitchen. I interrupted, "Nicole, I need to talk to you." She knew something serious was going on by the tone of my voice. For the next hour I explained Isabella's entire case to her and everything that had happened. In the end, she was as mad as I. She knew how hard I worked and couldn't believe these two would do this to me. I said, "It will be so hard, but I need to let it go. I'm going to keep my distance from Lieutenant Lewis and Sergeant Elker." Nicole knew me better and knew I would be thinking about this for years to come.

A month went by and I heard that Sergeant Elker's narcotic guys visited Isabella in federal prison. When Isabella walked into the visiting room, she expected to see Detective Mack and I. Instead, she saw two strangers. She hesitantly sat down across the table from them, wondering who they were and what they wanted.

Isabella asked, "Where are Detectives Mack and Greer?"

"They're no longer involved," one of them replied. "We'll be your new contacts."

Isabella quietly stood up, looked both men square in the eyes and said, "Fuck you—I'll do my time!" And she abruptly walked out.

Beyond having another solid case and another notch on the belt for the department, I couldn't help but feel bad for her. Detective Mack and I had assured her we would be involved while she worked off her case without endangering her family. She now faced the possibility of a twenty-five-year sentence in state prison and law enforcement would miss out on a valuable informant.

*****

Months after I gave up Isabella's case, I thought the worst was behind me, but I was wrong. I took the sergeant promotional test and felt I had a good shot of being promoted. There were a total of thirteen candidates, and more than half of them had nowhere near the experience I had. Part of the promotional process was an internal evaluation by the current sergeants in the department. Sergeant Elker and some of his friends were part of this process. They rated me so low that I never had a chance. I ended up at the bottom; thirteenth on a list of thirteen candidates.

I was now emotionally down and in a very low part in my career. I wanted to be left alone. I purposely assigned myself to graveyard patrol to get away from all the negativity. My body was overridden by stress and I developed an irregular heartbeat. This led to many surgeries in an attempt to stabilize my heart.

I made a decision to take care of my family, work hard, and mind my own business. I had little hope that things would ever change. One of my former supervisors from the undercover details,

Lieutenant Dalton, kept reminding me to be patient, but I knew Isabella Herrera's federal prison sentence would be completed within a year and a half and then she'd move to the state system. *What a waste. She'll never get an opportunity to work her case off,* I thought.

*****

Nearly a year had passed since the current chief, the outsider, resigned. This time the city manager promoted from within our ranks and selected a very competent man for the job. David Flannagan was now our new chief of police. Chief Flannagan, known for his easygoing personality, was fair, very intelligent, and modest.

It wasn't more than a month into his tenure as chief when he made some very positive, and needed, changes within the department. One of the first things he did was reassign Lieutenant Dalton to head our narcotic and crime impact undercover teams. Lieutenant Lewis, who had lied about me and derailed our case with Isabella Herrera, retired. Lieutenant Dalton was not a fan of Sergeant Elker and he knew it, so he reassigned himself out of the division.

I was now working day watch patrol and couldn't be happier that Chief Flannagan was promoted. I had never worked for him and didn't know him personally, but I heard he appreciated hard work and rewarded it. I certainly liked his recent personnel reassignments too. One afternoon, Torrance dispatch broadcast for me to respond to the station and meet Lieutenant Dalton in his office.

I drove to the station, wondering what he wanted. I knew it wasn't negative, as Lieutenant Dalton and I had developed a friendship over the years. He continued to look after all the guys, including myself, who had worked on the undercover teams during his tenure. I figured he just wanted to catch up on life.

When I made my way toward his office, I recalled the last time I was there. It was when Lieutenant Lewis threatened to have me terminated for having an affair with Isabella Herrera if I didn't turn over her case file. Not a good memory! I walked into the waiting area and saw our secretary, Kathy, with headphones on transcribing something on the computer. I said hello, but she couldn't hear me.

I finally said hello loud enough for her to hear. She jumped up and gave me a warm hug. She said, "Tommy! It is so good to see you! It's been hell here for the past few years."

I smiled and said, "Yeah, but there's a new sheriff in town." She smiled from ear to ear.

I informed Kathy that Lieutenant Dalton wanted to see me. As I walked into his office, I had a grin and said, "You look much better than the last guy who sat behind that big desk."

Lieutenant Dalton laughed and said, "I hope so."

I sat down and we caught up on our family life. Lieutenant Dalton had a mischievous grin on his face while he talked to me. I knew something was up and was waiting for him to stop teasing me and get to the point.

He reached behind his desk, picked up a large case file, and dropped it on top of his desk. I recognized the case file to be that of Isabella Herrera's. Lieutenant Dalton looked right at me and said, "Tommy, let's go get her!"

I almost lost it. My emotions were on edge, to say the least. Part of me wanted nothing to do with the case, but the other part of me wanted to jump back in because I respected the man before me, and I wanted to make him proud. I also wanted to fulfill the agreement we had made with Isabella.

Lieutenant Dalton said, "I told Chief Flannagan all about the case. I filled him in on how you got screwed and were falsely accused of having an affair with an informant who was in federal prison. Chief Flannagan told me to get you on board and make some cases."

I said, "I'll do anything you want me to do, but I'm not sure I want to be involved. Detective Mack's narcotic team and your narcotic crew should work the case together."

Lieutenant Dalton agreed but said, "I really want you to bring Isabella back on board."

After thinking it over, I realized that this felt right, so it didn't take long for me to agree. I said, "Let's fly up to the federal prison in Seattle, and I'll do the introduction. Isabella trusts Detective Mack and I'm pretty sure she'd be willing to work her case off as long as he's involved."

Lieutenant Dalton said, "I wouldn't have it any other way."

"Isabella's time in federal custody will be up within a year. Then she'll be transferred into the California state prison system. If she gets that far, it will be too late for her to work her case off."

"Understood. Go pack your bags. We're leaving for Seattle to pay Ms. Herrera a visit."

"Let me know the time and date—I'll be there," I said.

*****

A week later, Lieutenant Dalton and I, along with his new narcotic sergeant, Sergeant Jaggard, were on a United Airlines flight to Seattle. I had one day to introduce Lieutenant Dalton and Sergeant Jaggard to Isabella and hopefully gain back her confidence in us. Our flight touched down in the rainy city at 11:30 a.m. We rented a car and drove straight to the SeaTac Federal Detention Center.

We didn't want to attract any unnecessary attention by cutting to the front of the line and identifying ourselves as law enforcement, so we waited in line for an hour with everyone else. We filled out paperwork before we were cleared to go in, and then we were told to follow the yellow line to the visitors' area where we were directed to table 7. The weather had cleared up, so the prison staff opened the outside visiting area, which was better for privacy because everyone could spread out. Inside these facilities, the walls are cement and sounds echo off them.

Lieutenant Dalton, Sergeant Jaggard, and I all sat on the same side of the table where we could observe inmates as they walked in. When Isabella entered, she immediately recognized me and walked toward our table with a smile on her face. As she got closer, her face suddenly dropped. She looked beyond me and said in a stern, yet quiet voice, "Get him the hell out of here!"

I looked to my left at Lieutenant Dalton and Sergeant Jaggard just beyond him. I gestured toward Sergeant Jaggard and asked, "Him?"

Isabella was on edge and nodded. "Yes. Him. He looks like a cop."

I turned to Lieutenant Dalton, and he asked Sergeant Jaggard to wait for us outside. I felt bad for him, but we only had one shot at this, and we needed to start on the right foot. I noticed that only a quarter of the tables had inmates and visitors sitting at them. I also observed several inmates watching us.

Lieutenant Dalton and I stood up, and Isabella's demeanor changed immediately. She smiled and greeted us with open arms as she spoke in Spanish loud enough for the others to hear. She rounded the table and took a seat across from us, and then we sat down. "I had to put on a show to cover myself. I want the others to think were related," she said in English, speaking in a quiet tone.

I introduced Isabella to Lieutenant Dalton and explained that he was one of my bosses when we worked her and her organization. Isabella respected us because she knew how thorough we had been building cases against her. Isabella nodded and smiled at Lieutenant Dalton. She said, "I apologize for kicking your friend out, but he did look like a cop."

Isabella nodded at me and Lieutenant Dalton and said, "You guys look more Colombian."

I laughed and said, "But we don't speak much Spanish. We need Detective Mack here for that."

Isabella asked, "What the hell happened to you and Mack?"

I explained, "It is a long story, but a new narcotic crew came in and wanted your case. I refused to give it to them because Detective Mack had your case file. The lieutenant in charge of that team read your letters and accused me of having an affair with you."

Isabella almost screamed as she laughed. I told her how the new narcotic sergeant had heard I had a major Colombian informant and how he thought his team should work her because it was a Torrance case. "The team had no experience, and I wanted no part of it. I knew they'd screw it up and more than likely get your family killed. The lieutenant and his sergeant saw the little hearts with the happy face in your letters and used that to say we were too close."

Isabella shook her head in disbelief.

I added, "The lieutenant of the narcotic team told me he was going to fire me if I didn't hand you over to them. I was thinking about fighting it because I knew I'd be cleared, but it would have dragged on for a long time and ruined my career. I ended up giving them your file. I knew you'd tell them to get lost."

Isabella said, "Two guys, who looked like cops, came here and told me you and Detective Mack were no longer in the picture and I had to work with them. I immediately got up and told them, 'No fucking way—I'd rather do my time.' Are you going to help me now?"

We spent the next two hours talking about Lieutenant Dalton overseeing the Torrance narcotic team now. Isabella smiled upon hearing this news, so I was pretty sure we had her. "Detective Mack and Lieutenant Pagh are still working on the narcotic task force and they're up and running on all cylinders," I said.

Lieutenant Dalton added, "Depending on how big of a case you bring forward, most likely Detective Mack's team and my narcotic team will work the case together."

Isabella responded, "I like that. I trust Detective Mack."

Lieutenant Dalton used that opening to tell Isabella, "By the way, Detective Mack said hello and wanted you to know his team is ready." Isabella smiled again. Lieutenant Dalton assured Isabella his Torrance narcotic team had experienced detectives and were ready to work her cases too.

I asked Isabella, "Can you tell Lieutenant Dalton the short version of how you were held captive in Michoacán, Mexico, by the Federales for almost a year? And tell him how you escaped and ended up being arrested in New Jersey?" I knew Lieutenant Dalton had already heard all this from me and from reading her file, but I wanted him to hear it directly from Isabella.

After she told her story, Lieutenant Dalton said, "I have a few questions."

"Sure, fire away."

"I know you had run a big portion of the Colombian cocaine empire in the Western United States. What did you do when someone ripped you off?"

"Are you asking me if I have ever killed anyone?"

"Yes."

Isabella looked straight at him and her eyes turned cold. "I have never put my hands on anyone. If someone betrayed us, they just disappeared and I never knew how."

Lieutenant Dalton kicked me under the table as he proceeded to ask another question. "I was working on the Thanksgiving night when you met with other people at a restaurant in the Valley. Do you remember that evening?"

"Yes, I do. I also recall seeing someone follow me. I was scared, so I had paid a lady five hundred dollars to drive me down to the border and into Mexico. It was well known in the business that law enforcement wouldn't follow us there."

Lieutenant Dalton asked her, "Why would it be a problem?"

"The Federales are crooked, and people are hungry for money there. They wouldn't hesitate to kill a cop from America for pennies." She looked at me and said, "Detective Greer, here, and Detective Mack would be crazy to go to Mexico."

Isabella proceeded to say that we were marked men because all the reports of our arrests had our names on them. She said, "Colombian drug cartels have attorneys on retainer in America for two reasons. One, when their drug cartel members are arrested with a significant amount of money or cocaine, the attorneys' job is to represent that person and keep them quiet. Secondly, the attorneys also obtain all reports from the arrest and send them back to Colombia, where they keep the names of the cops involved."

She continued, "You see, if Detective Mack or Detective Greer are in Mexico and are recognized by someone from the past, they themselves would disappear. Or worse yet, if they are with their family, their family would disappear too." She looked at me and said, "My advice to you is to never go to Mexico." I stared straight at her and didn't say a word.

Lieutenant Dalton asked Isabella, "If people disappear when they betray the bosses back home in Colombia, aren't you afraid of you or your family disappearing if we put a deal together?"

Isabella's expression turned serious. She leaned across the table, closing the distance between us. She said, "I won't betray anyone from my homeland. I have a big payback for the Mexicans that held me captive for a year. I swore when the Mexicans crossed me, I would get my revenge."

Lieutenant Dalton said, "Let me make something very clear. We will not condone anyone being killed based on revenge."

Isabella shook her head and said, "You don't understand! The revenge will be from the arrest of those Mexicans and their families that turned me in. It will be when their drugs and money are confiscated and they are put behind bars, like I am."

Lieutenant Dalton nodded and said, "I can deal with that. So how will this work? How will you inform us about who we need to follow or which location we need to look into?"

"It will happen like this— in a letter, I'll ask you to meet uncle so-and-so at a certain address, or I'll have someone contact you and tell you who to keep an eye on."

Lieutenant Dalton said, "That will work."

Isabella continued, "The people you'll be looking into won't be in the city of Torrance or even close to it."

"It will have to be in California though."

Isabella agreed, "Yes, it will be in California. The people you will be following, and hopefully arresting, will be Mexicans. Mexicans that put me through hell."

"Understood."

Just then, an intercom came on and announced that visiting hours were over.

We stood and Isabella hugged us both, speaking in Spanish loud enough for the other inmates to hear. Neither Lieutenant Dalton nor I had a clue what she said, but we knew it was for show.

We walked out of the prison and found Sergeant Jaggard back at the rental car. Lieutenant Dalton apologized to him for asking him to leave. He was a good sport and said, "I guess I'll have to work on my appearance." We all laughed.

As we drove to our hotel, Lieutenant Dalton looked at me and warned, "Never go to Mexico—You'll be a dead man."

"I definitely heard her loud and clear."

We arrived at our hotel and checked in. Then we walked across the street to a local bar, had a few beers, and played some pool.

The next morning, we checked out of our hotel, drove back to the airport, and returned the rental car. We had a few hours before our flight left, so we all dosed off, humped over in our seats in the terminal. Sergeant Jaggard woke up and heard the last call warning, "Passengers Jaggard, Dalton, and Greer." We barely made our flight home.

On the return flight, I told Lieutenant Dalton the trip was successful. I added, "If you need anything, just let me know. But it looks like you guys have this handled."

"Don't worry. I'll keep you in the loop."

CHAPTER
48

Two weeks later, I was working day watch uniform patrol when I got a call from Torrance dispatch on my police car radio. They told me that Lieutenant Pagh needed to speak to me ASAP and instructed me to call his cell phone.

I quickly found a pay phone across the street from the police station and called Lieutenant Pagh. Because Lieutenant Pagh was a lieutenant and running a multiagency task force, he had a portable phone. I called and he answered on the first ring.

Typically, Lieutenant Pagh was a low-key person, but that day, I could hear a little excitement in his voice. He said, "Tommy, I'm short on time so I'll try to make this quick. I'm going to make your day," he said.

I responded, "Good!"

Lieutenant Pagh explained that his task force, along with Lieutenant Dalton's team, was working a case Isabella had given them. My heart started pumping. He said, "My team just followed a large Ryder moving truck from a ranch house on the United States side of the border, near Mexico."

He continued, "We're not sure if there's anything in the Ryder truck, so we've got to be careful. We can't just stop the truck and search it unless we have a legitimate reason. If we stop the Ryder truck on a hunch without visibly seeing a reason to stop it, we'd have to let the driver go—he'd no doubt call the people at the ranch, and the operation would be shut down. Timing's everything, Tommy—There's a reason you're working uniform patrol today. I need someone like you who knows what they are doing."

"What do you need me to do?" I asked.

He said, "You won't believe it—Right now, as we're speaking, the truck pulled into the Marriott parking lot and parked illegally in a no-parking zone. This gives us a reason to make contact with the driver. I'm going to have Marriot security call Torrance dispatch and ask them to send an officer out to make contact with the driver for parking illegally in the red zone. Tommy, you'll be the one dispatched to the call. I'll let you take it from there. If you can find a way to see what's in the enclosed bed of the truck without cluing in the driver, that'd be great."

I said, "Understood. I'm at a pay phone just down the street, so I'm close by."

"Good. Wait until dispatch calls before you head over."

Before Lieutenant Pagh hung up the phone, he said, "In some way, Isabella Herrera must have been involved in having this Ryder truck driver come all the way up to Torrance from the border to park illegally."

"It wouldn't surprise me if she had been, but what makes you think so?"

Lieutenant Pagh replied, "The driver is just sitting there, and his head is on a swivel. He looks like he's on high alert—like he's waiting for someone."

"Or thinks he's waiting for someone," I said.

"You're probably right, Tommy. This is crazy, man. Crazy!" He then hung up the phone.

I sat in my patrol car, waiting for Torrance's dispatch to detail me to the Marriott. As I waited, I smiled and thought how smart and conniving Isabella was. She said she'd get payback on the Mexicans who had put her through hell, and I believed this was just the start. *God help those poor bastards.*

Finally, Torrance dispatch came over my patrol car radio and sent me to the Torrance Marriot regarding an illegally parked full-size

Ryder truck in the red zone. I advised dispatch, "Copy that. I'm five minutes away."

When I arrived at the Marriott, I laughed, as the full-size Ryder truck couldn't have been more out of place. Not only was it parked in a no-parking zone, but it was also partially blocking traffic. I pulled up behind the truck and turned on my overhead lights.

As I got out of my patrol car, I could see the driver eyeing me in the driver's-side mirror. I wish I had a camera, as his eyes were as big as silver dollars. His expression alone told me all I needed to know; there was something in this truck he didn't want me to see. I exited my patrol car and slowly walked to the back of the truck bed and stopped. The driver watched every move I made.

As I stood there, I noticed an overpowering odor of marijuana emitting from the truck bed—and it smelled strong! It was obvious this truck contained a lot of marijuana. I reached for my portable radio in my waistband and requested Torrance dispatch to send a couple more officers to my location. Torrance's dispatch acknowledged my request and dispatched two more officers to help me.

In my broken Spanish, I got the driver's attention and told him to hold his hands out of the driver's-side window so I could see them. Just then, two assisting officers arrived on scene. I told both to come to my location at the rear of the Ryder truck.

When the officers stood next to me, one said, "Wow! Can you smell that marijuana?"

I laughed and said, "That's why I requested you guys. Let's get the driver out of the truck."

I ordered the driver to exit his door while showing me his hands the entire time. I had him slowly walk backwards toward me, then I handcuffed him. The other officers cleared the front of the cab, making sure there were no other passengers. The driver was nervous and sweat was beading on his forehead. He spoke very little English, so I requested another officer, Hector Mata, who spoke fluent Spanish, to my location.

When Officer Mata arrived, I stepped away from the driver, so he couldn't hear what I had to say to Officer Mata. "There's a strong smell of marijuana coming from the bed of the truck. This investigation has to be textbook perfect, so I'll ask the questions to the driver. I'll need you to translate exactly what I say," I said.

We uncuffed the driver and as I spoke, Officer Mata translated in Spanish.

"I need to see your driver's license and the registration of the truck."

"I don't have a driver's license," the driver said.

"What's your name?"

"Jesus Diaz."

I asked, "Do you have any identification on you?"

He reached into his pocket, pulled out his wallet, and gave me a temporary California identification card with the name Jesus Diaz on it with a San Diego address.

I asked, "Did you rent this truck yourself? And if not, who did?"

"No, I didn't. I don't know who rented it."

"What brings you to Torrance? And specifically, why did you come to this Marriott and park in the no-parking zone?"

Diaz replied, "My friend Eduardo paid me to drive the truck up from San Diego."

"What part of San Diego? And where did you pick up the truck from?"

"I picked up the truck from Eduardo at a Home Depot parking lot in northern San Diego."

"What's Eduardo's last name."

"I don't know."

"Why did you come to this Marriott and park illegally?"

"Eduardo gave me specific instructions to drive to this Marriott and park the truck in the red zone. I was told to wait for someone to contact me."

I asked Diaz, "Do you know what's in the bed of the truck?"

He shook his head no.

"Since you don't have a valid California driver's license, I cannot let you drive the truck."

He nodded acknowledging he understood.

"Before I impound the truck, I'll have to take inventory of all contents and then I'll give you a receipt," I said.

He agreed.

I walked to the roll door at the back of the truck, jumped up onto the bed's edge, and pulled open the roll door. In all my six years of working undercover and seizing tons of drugs and money, I'd never seen anything like this. The truck was filled top to bottom with what appeared to be individually wrapped insulation rolls, each one three-foot in diameter. The marijuana smell was pungent. Then I took a closer look. These circular rolls didn't reveal insulation at all, but rather high-grade marijuana.

Diaz was immediately arrested and transported to the Torrance Police Department jail, and the truck was impounded and stored at the Torrance Police Department. A little over eight tons of high-grade marijuana was recovered.

Lieutenant Pagh met me at the Torrance Police Department to see the marijuana for himself. He couldn't believe it. He said, "Tommy, this couldn't have worked out better. I've already notified Lieutenant Dalton and Detective Mack. They were surveilling the ranch house where this Ryder truck came from. Detective Mack and one of Lieutenant Dalton's narcotic guys are writing the search warrant for the ranch house as we speak."

I smiled at Lieutenant Pagh, pointed to the eight tons of marijuana and said, "If this is any indication of what's in that ranch house, this is going to be an epic bust."

Later that night, once Detective Mack completed his search warrant, I was told to drive to the border to assist. I was in uniform and drove my black-and-white. The ranch house was on about one hundred acres of land, and in addition to the main house, there were several bunkhouses and one large barn.

At 11:55 p.m., about twenty narcotic detectives from Lieutenant Pagh's and Dalton's teams, along with DEA and US Customs agents, executed a search warrant for the ranch property. The search of the barn resulted in a seizure of over two tons of pure cocaine packaged and ready for shipment throughout the United States. A little over two million dollars in United States currency was recovered from one of the bunkhouses.

Another unbelievable discovery was under a false floor in the barn. There we found a sophisticated tunnel leading from the barn into the country of Mexico. The tunnel was about half a mile long and had an elaborate ventilation system. The floor of the tunnel had a small railroad track for large carts, which carried drugs from Mexico into the barn in the United States.

I helped arrest and interview the two owners of the property who were sleeping in the main house when the search warrant was served. We also arrested ten others who were sleeping in the bunkhouses. When I interviewed the husband-and-wife owners of the property, it all came *full circle* to me.

The wife, Margarita Perez, revealed she was born and raised in Michoacán, Mexico. She said her maiden name was Hernandez. She said her brother Conrado Hernandez still lived in Michoacán. Her sister, Manuela Pena, was living in Murrieta, California, but was currently in prison for drug trafficking, along with her husband, Arturo Pena.

I could barely keep my composure as I interviewed her. I kept thinking about Isabella Herrera's determination to not betray her fellow Colombians while working her case off. She stayed true to her word and got revenge on the people who betrayed her, held her captive, and tormented her for a year in Mexico.

Specifically, Isabella got payback on Conrado Hernandez by exploiting his new drug operation, resulting in the arrest of his sister. Somehow, I didn't think this was the end of it. If I were Conrado Hernandez, I'd be looking over my shoulder!

CHAPTER
49

It was a beautiful summer day at the beach. The sky was clear, the sun was warm, and the water glistened. Nicole sat on an oversized beach towel. She wore sunglasses and was slathered in sunscreen. She looked toward the shore. Her smile widened. She had waited for this moment for a long time.

Danielle and Erik lay on their surfboards, hoping to catch a wave, not far from the shoreline. I was wading beside them. "Here comes a swell!" The swell became a wave that propelled the kids toward shore. They skimmed ahead of the breaking wave. I body-surfed along with them. We hit the sand and gathered ourselves up. It was a great ride.

We waved to Nicole. The kids were excited to show off their skills on their boards. Nicole waved back.

CHAPTER
50

It was November of 1995 at one forty-five on a rainy afternoon in Seattle, Washington. Isabella Herrera walked out of SeaTac Federal Detention Center and looked up toward the sky. She opened her mouth to catch a few raindrops on her tongue and said to herself, "Nothing like the sweet taste of freedom."

EPILOGUE

After Isabella's release from prison, she was never seen or heard from again. Gilberto and Miguel Rodriguez were apprehended by Colombian national police in 1995. They were sent to Bogotá's La Picota prison. Gilberto was extradited to the United States in 2004. He eventually accepted a thirty-year prison sentence under a plea deal and died in prison. Miguel was extradited to the US in 2005 and was sentenced to 30 years in federal prison.

Tommy Greer moved up the ranks and became captain of the Torrance Police Department. He retired in 2012. He remains happily married to Nicole in their South Bay home.

ACKNOWLEDGMENTS

Full Circle would not have been completed if it were not for my wife, Monique, my daughter, Danielle, and my son-in-law, Colton. All encouraged me to write my story. Special thanks and love also to my beautiful son, Erik, who motivated me to complete this book right up to the time of his passing.

This book would not have been completed without my talented childhood friend Brandon Rosin, whose knowledge and guidance made Full Circle come to life! To my editors, my wife Monique and friend Roberta Clark, thank you for the many hours you put toward this novel. Special thanks to Dave Marsden, Dennis Addington, and Jimmy Packard who helped me with this work, but also for your mentorship during this time and life itself. I am so grateful to all my TPD teammates and supervisors, who let me be a part of this historical team. These men were the ultimate professionals. Their dedication and sacrifices to the people they served were unparalleled. I was fortunate to have worked with them.

ABOUT THE AUTHOR

Capt. Bradley T. Wilson was born and raised in Redondo Beach, California, and still resides in Southern California with his wife Monique. He spent nearly thirty years in law enforcement. He worked with two highly decorated undercover surveillance teams, whose arrests and seizures of millions of dollars in drugs, money, and property, along with the apprehension of hundreds of career criminals, will most likely never be matched in his department. Brad is retired and spends his time with his wife traveling and in the Pacific Ocean paddling, surfing, and swimming.

Printed in the USA
CPSIA information can be obtained
at www.ICGtesting.com
JSHW082323310524
64029JS00001B/2

9 781639 859092